RAYNER W. MARKLEY
WILLARD D. SHEELER

Spot Drills

ILLUSTRATED GRAMMAR EXERCISES

3

Oxford University Press

Oxford University Press

200 Madison Avenue
New York, NY 10016 USA

Walton Street
Oxford OX2 6DP England

OXFORD is a trademark of Oxford University Press.

Library of Congress Cataloging-in-Publication Data
(Revised for vol. 3)

Markley, Rayner W.
  Spot drills.

  Vol. 3 by Rayner W. Markley
  Contents: 1. Low intermediate—   — 3. Illustrated
  grammar exercises.
    1. English language—Text-books for foreign speakers.
  2. English language—Grammar—1950–   . I. Sheeler,
  Willard De Mont, 1915–   . II. Title.
  PE1128.M337   1983   428.2'4   83-2264
  ISBN 0-19-434125-9 (pbk. : v. 1)
        0-19-434126-7 (pbk. : v. 2)
        0-19-434127-5 (pbk. : v. 3)

Editor: Margot Gramer
Associate Editor: Mary Lynne Simyak
Illustrations by Marie-Hélène Jeeves.
Typeset by Oxprint.

Printing (last digit): 9 8 7 6 5 4
Printed in Hong Kong

PREFACE

Spot Drills 3 provides practice material on specific grammatical points for learners of English as a Second Language. It is designed for use with any major textbook series or as self-study practice.

The 75 one-page units of *Spot Drills 3* cover grammatical structures and forms usually taught at an intermediate to advanced level. The emphasis is on spoken language rather than the more formal written style; however, many of the structures in this book are appropriate to both. The units are arranged in four sections: (1) Points concerning noun phrases (phrase modifiers of nouns, relative clauses, adjective modifiers); (2) Points concerning verb phrases (modal auxiliaries, passive voice, infinitive complements and clause complements of verbs); (3) Points concerning adverbial clauses (cause, purpose, condition, concession, degree), subjunctive clauses, and indirect speech; and (4) Sentences that have two clauses (two relative clauses, a noun clause within a relative clause, a relative clause within an appositive).

It is not intended or necessary to do the units in order. One can start anywhere and skip around as needed. This is facilitated by the page-by-page format. However, the drills do progress somewhat in difficulty, culminating with those in Section 4, which has students producing longer sentences and more complicated structures.

The use of vocabulary in this book is somewhat less restrained than that in *Spot Drills 1* and *2*. Although much of it deals with commonly known things, other words are used in order to add interest for more advanced students, and sometimes special words and expressions are necessary to keep the language natural. The teacher may wish to preview certain items if it is anticipated that unknown vocabulary might impede understanding and interrupt the smooth operation of the drills. The integral pictures and tables featured aid in understanding the vocabulary.

The Drills

The term "drills" is used loosely; it includes not only mechanical, or fluency, drills, but also exercises which require making a choice or creating sentences. Often there is a progression in the unit from a simpler, more mechanical operation to the formation of an entire sentence or both a question and its answer. There are three principal types of drills in this book.

Fill-in exercises require that a correct word or phrase be added to complete a sentence (e.g., 2B). Sometimes a word must be chosen from a list and then filled in (e.g., 1A).

Sentence formation exercises require that complete sentences be formed like an example sentence (e.g., 4B). Often a word given in parentheses or selected from a list must be used in the sentence (e.g., 15A). Sometimes sentence parts must be matched in order to form a sentence (e.g., 9A). At other times, the student must add a function word to the sentence being formed (e.g., 4B). In some cases, the student forms a sentence that is a sequel to one given in the exercises (e.g., 18C).

Sentence combination exercises require that one sentence be embedded into another as a subordinate clause (e.g., 50A). The student may need to decide which of the given sentences is to be subordinated (e.g., 53C).

Many drills have a provision for two students to take part. These consist of a question and an answer (e.g., 2C) or a statement and a response. In other cases, the student forms a sentence that is a logical extension of one given in the exercise (e.g., 9B).

Natural responses should be used for replies in any exercise. This means making any necessary pronoun substitutions and shortening of predicates. If full sentences sound stilted in some cases, the exercise can be done again with short answers. With all full sentences particular attention should be paid to the proper placement of sentence stress. Undoubtedly students will need help in this regard; notes in the Answer Key give some guidance to the teacher in this area. A completed example is given for every drill, and students should, of course, always study and understand it before proceeding.

The use of pictures or tables in *Spot Drills 3* allows for considerable communication practice and creativity on the part of the student. Many drills do not have a single correct answer, and different students may get slightly different information from the pictures or tables.

Expanding the Drills

Many drills can be expanded; that is, they can be done again in a slightly different way. Sometimes sentences can be lengthened by adding phrases or entire clauses. For example, the phrase *according to the chart* can be added to sentences in 2A (Most of the parks, according to the chart, have camping.). Some drills can be extended by using the sentence cues, pictures, or tables of other drills. For example, the table for 2A can be used with 4C (We want to go to a park with camping and hiking.).

Another way to vary a drill is to make it into a question-and-answer drill. As an example, 1A can be changed from statements to questions (Did the Carlberg Company make those switches? Yes, but they didn't make any other parts.).

It is especially useful for students to improvise a variation of a drill after they have become familiar with the vocabulary it contains. For example, the students can answer the questions just formed in 1A by putting their own words in the blanks. At the end of an exercise, it is always good to have the students create one or two sentences relating to their personal experience.

Answer Key

At the back of the book is a complete Answer Key, making *Spot Drills 3* an ideal home-study book. There are answers to all of the drills, including suggested answers for the open-ended drills. On the inside back cover is a summary table of past and perfect tenses. There are no general grammatical explanations in the book. However, the boxed examples at the beginning of each unit do illustrate what each unit is about. It is expected that the teacher will provide whatever is needed before doing these drills, and the teacher is given some help by notes incorporated into the Answer Key.

The drills can be used in a variety of language learning situations to supplement courses organized from widely different approaches. Whether coming to a new grammatical topic or spotting a need for extra practice, the teacher can quickly turn to the appropriate Spot Drill.

October 1986   R.W.M.   W.D.S.

CONTENTS

Section Three   ADVERBIAL CLAUSES

1 Modifiers: Before other

some other kind	**some** other
my other shoe	**my** other (one)
ten other books	**ten** other(s) (ones)

A. Fill in the blanks with the modifier in parentheses, **other**, and a noun from the list.

> animals clothes daughters states team
> city countries parts suggestion trips

1. The Carlberg Company made these switches, but they didn't make **any other parts**. (any)
2. India will organize a conference on disease control, and _____ will join it. (16)
3. Joyce is in college. _____ are still in high school. (our)
4. California's population is increasing rapidly. _____ are also growing very fast. (several)
5. Only my shirts are clean. _____ are all dirty. (my)
6. We enjoyed our Caribbean tour. We'll be taking _____ in the future. (some)
7. Tigers usually live alone, but _____ live in herds or family groups. (many)
8. The Giants admit women to their games free on Wednesday afternoons. _____ does that. (no)
9. Only Miami and Tampa require a license for this. _____ has such a law. (no)
10. I don't think that's a good idea, but _____ is worth a try. (your)

B. Fill in the blanks with the modifier in parentheses and **other(s)** or **other one(s)**.

1. This kind of seal is quite dangerous. **Most others** are not dangerous at all. (most)
2. Ten people were killed in the accident. _____ died later in the hospital. (three)
3. These aren't the only boots on sale. There are _____ in the next aisle. (many)
4. These peaches aren't very ripe. Please go back and pick out _____. (some)
5. I'm going to buy these shoes. _____ don't quite fit right. (those)
6. I just drive this car around town. I use _____ for long trips. (my)
7. I like this seat better. _____ was too far back. (that)
8. I've read several of Poe's stories, including "The Black Cat," "The Gold Bug," and _____. (a few)
9. Use this machine. _____ are out of order. (those)
10. Two pockets are full and _____ has a handkerchief in it. (one)

C. Fill in the blanks with a modifier + **other (one)** or **others**.

1. One egg hatched after 28 days. **Two others** hatched on the 29th day.
2. My math course is not going so well. _____ are going better.
3. This is a luxury car. _____ is an economy car.
4. The first battle was easy to win. _____ were hard and costly.

2 Quantifiers: Before of Phrases

most of my time
many of them

A. Form sentences about the state parks. Use the words given and the quantifiers **all**, **most**, **some**, **a few**, **a couple**, or **none**.

Ex. camping
Most of the parks have camping.

1. an entrance fee
2. fishing
3. guides
4. hiking
5. hunting
6. picnic areas
7. rest rooms

State Parks						
	Fee	Picnic Areas	Camping	Hiking	Fishing	Guide
Park A	x	x		x	x	
Park B	x	x	x	x	x	x
Park C	x	x	x	x		
Park D	x	x	x	x		
Park E		x		x		
Park F	x	x	x		x	
Park G	x	x	x		x	x

NOTE: No hunting in any park. All parks have rest rooms.

B. Form noun phrases from the words in parentheses. Then fill in the blanks.

1. We knew many of the Latin dances, but we didn't know **a lot of the other ones**. (the/ones/other/of/a/lot)
2. Some of Rosa's old pants fit just right, but _____ are too short. (her/many/of/ones/other)
3. A few students signed up for after-school activities. _____ went home. (most/of/ones/other/the)
4. That looks like a good TV, but I like _____ better. (both/of/others/these)
5. My friend was looking at cars. He liked the sports car, but he didn't think much of _____. (any/of/others/the)
6. I want ten pounds of this coffee, but _____. (kind/less/of/the/other)
7. Jane's taking three courses. She's failing one, but she's doing very well in _____. (both/her/of/ones/other)
8. Give me a little of this kind of candy, but _____. (a/lot/of/other/that)
9. These two children have dark hair. _____ are blondes. (all/of/other/my/students)
10. I'd like four pounds of those Winesap apples and _____. (a/few/of/ones/other/these)

C. Student 1: read the statement. Student 2: ask a question with **how many** or **how much**.
Student 1: answer with a full sentence. Use **of them** or **of it**.

Ex. She bought a dozen doughnuts. (four)
How many did she eat?
She ate four of them.

1. My sister had about 50 stamps for sale or trade. (most)
2. Washington High played 22 basketball games this year. (14)
3. I took two tests this morning. (both)
4. The cab driver found $100 in the back of his cab. (none)
5. Our cows produce 100 gallons of milk a day. (all)

3 Modifiers of Nouns: Compound Modifiers with Numbers

a **six-foot** man
a **six-state** manhunt

A. Form noun phrases. Use one item from each column.

Number	Unit	Noun
two	gallon	temperature
seven	mile	airplane trip
ten	foot	gasoline tank
15	hour	basketball player
25	ounce	bottle of soda
32	pound	movie
90	degree	sack of rice
2000	story	building

Ex. a two-hour movie

B. Read each statement. Student 1: ask a yes/no question using the word in parentheses. Student 2: answer with **no** and a full sentence. Use a compound modifier with a number.

Ex. His book cost ten dollars. (five)
Did he buy a five-dollar book?
No, he bought a ten-dollar book.

1. Her car's engine has six cylinders. (four)
2. Mr. Marshall went to a conference for five days. (seven)
3. The professor's lecture lasted two hours. (one-half)
4. The bus carries 50 passengers. (40)
5. Jane's reading a book with 480 pages. (200)
6. Those pots hold two quarts. (three)
7. The freight train has 100 cars. (85)
8. Her long distance phone call lasted 20 minutes. (nine)
9. The rope was 30 feet long. (45)

C. Form noun phrases to label the pictures. Use the words given to form compound modifiers with numbers.

1. door
   A four-door car.
2. speed
3. story
4. cent
5. hour
6. lane

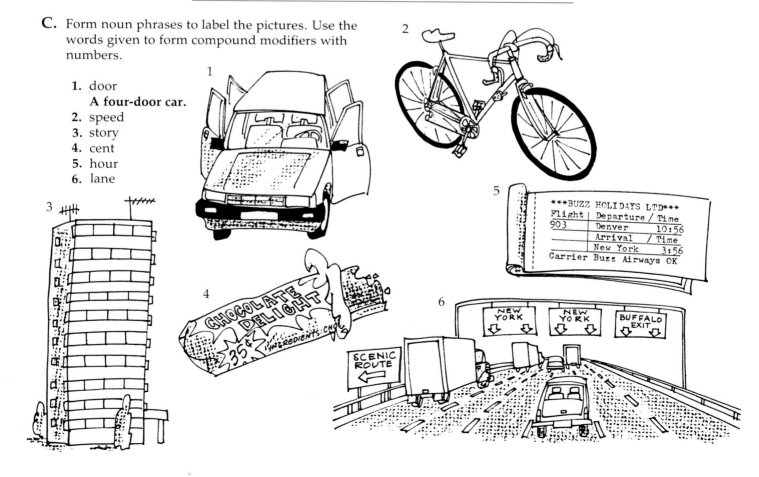

4 Modifiers of Nouns: Prepositional Phrases

the glass **on that shelf**
a glass **with a crack**

A. Match nouns 1–12 with modifying phrases a–l to form noun phrases.

1. the batteries	a. across the street
2. the ribbon	b. at sea
3. the hole	c. at the North Pole
4. the houses	d. by the window
5. those insects	e. in Ellen's hair
6. the lamp	f. in the flashlight
7. this picture	g. in this sweater
8. the planes	h. near the beach
9. that rash	i. on her skin
10. the ships	j. on the book cover
11. that clam bar	k. on the runway
12. the temperature	l. under that rock

1. **the batteries in the flashlight**

B. Form sentences about Ms. Brill's birthday gifts. Use a noun and a modifying phrase with **about, for, from, to, of, with** or **in**.

Ex. sweater/initials/Martha
She got a sweater with her initials from Martha.

1. book/gardening/Ted
2. two tickets/theater/Maria
3. gift certificate/sports store/Jim
4. box/candy/Miguel
5. make-up mirror/dresser/Judy
6. weekend/New York/her parents
7. wristwatch/second hand/her married sister

Now answer questions 8–10. Use **the one from**.

8. Which gift do you think she liked or needed more—the one from Martha or the one from Ted? The one from Jim or from Maria?
9. Which gift do you think she liked the most of all?
10. Which gift would you prefer for yourself?

C. Form sentences to tell which hotel you would like to stay at. Use **the one** + a prepositional phrase.

	Located near	Nightly rate	Entertainment	Features
Hotel Jersey	museum	$60.50	Merlin's Magic Show	game room
Lorton Lodge	stadium	$39.95	The Singing Cowboys	heated pool
Welton Hotel	beach	$49.95	Hawaiian band	free laundry

Ex. I'd like to stay at the one with the Hawaiian band.

5 Modifiers of Nouns: Infinitives

a book (for you) **to read**
the place (for her) **to buy coats**

A. Match nouns 1–8 with modifiers a–h to form noun phrases.

1.	a chair	a.	to wash
2.	a lot of money	b.	to finish
3.	a minute	c.	to iron
4.	one more window	d.	to re-cover
5.	some children	e.	to sit on
6.	some homework	f.	to spend
7.	some shirts	g.	to take care of
8.	some trash	h.	to throw out

1. a chair to sit on

B. Fill in the blanks with an appropriate infinitive.

1. I have an errand for you __to__ __do__.
2. The matter is settled. There is nothing more _____ _____.
3. There wasn't any coffee for us _____ _____.
4. We had some new kites for the children _____ _____ with.
5. Here's ten dollars _____ _____.
6. She had a bowl of cherries _____ _____.
7. Here's a clean sweater _____ _____.
8. Frank and Paula are looking for a place _____ _____.
9. The doctor prescribed medicine for Keiko _____ _____ three times a day.
10. I have five more letters _____ _____.

C. Student 1: ask a yes/no question. Student 2: answer with **no, (but)** and a full sentence. Use an infinitive.

Ex. a good time/invest in the stock market//buy real estate
Is this a good time to invest in the stock market?
No, but it's a good time to buy real estate.

1. a good place/keep my jewelry//hide money
2. a good company/do business with//work for
3. a good person/have on a hiking trip//have on board a ship
4. good paper/draw pictures on//type on
5. a good road/take to Springfield//take to Athens
6. a good beach/swim at//look for shells on
7. a good movie/see on Halloween//stay away from
8. a good place/have the business meeting//have the reception
9. the only time/see the art exhibit//get in free
10. a good place/order seafood//order steak

6 Modifiers of Nouns: Multiple Modifiers

that **homemade** cake **with raisins**
a **six-ton moving** crane **to sell**

A. Form noun phrases from the words in parentheses. Then fill in the blanks.

1. She ruined **the hand-painted design on her jacket**. (design/hand-painted/on her jacket/the)
2. He put some cream on _____. (aching/in his back/muscles/the)
3. He hasn't forgotten _____. (continuing/his/to be a pilot/wish)
4. I can't hand in _____. (about coal/half-finished/report/this)
5. They'll print _____. (letter/this/to the editor/well-written)
6. She's studying _____. (a/forgotten/of American history/period)
7. _____ will cost $3600. (their/30-day/to South America/trip)
8. She gave in to _____. (her/long-denied/to rest/need)
9. _____ bothered her. (birds/singing/by her window/some)
10. She's the proud mother of _____. (a/baby boy/ten-pound/with blue eyes)
11. We found the teacher in _____. (a/under a tree/spot/shady)
12. They're working on _____. (about the budget/questions/remaining/the)
13. Unfortunately, there is _____. (eight-lane/highway/an/to cross)
14. They're always using _____. (in the cabs/radios/the/two-way)
15. The painting has _____. (horses/many/running/with long tails)
16. The player had _____. (arm/bandaged/his/to watch out for)
17. _____ tasted very good. (at dinner/fish/smoked/the)
18. _____ is a good sign. (a/for the first night/packed/theater)
19. They showed _____ at noon. (a/advertisement/for Softie Soap/good/30-second)
20. They gave me _____. (round/spoon/this/with my name on it)

B. Student 1: ask a **what** question about each dinosaur. Student 2: answer with a noun phrase. Use two or three modifiers from the list.

flying	bony-plated	with a giant head
swimming	three-horned	with a snake-like neck
meat-eating	40-ton	with a terrible tail
plant-eating	20-foot-tall	with 25-foot wings

1. brontosaurus
   What was a brontosaurus?
   A 40-ton, plant-eating dinosaur.
2. stegosaurus
3. triceratops
4. tyrannosaurus

7 Adjectives: Used as Nouns

The old have wisdom, but not the strength of **the young**.

A. Fill in the blanks with **the** and an adjective from the list.

curious	weak
unusual	innocent
supernatural	impossible
guilty	suffering
deaf	strong

1. Printed words on the TV screen aid __the deaf__ .
2. Ripley's newspaper feature "Believe It or Not" is about _____.
3. Mary Diaz devotes her life as a nurse to _____.
4. That author always writes frightening stories about _____.
5. It can't work. Don't try to do _____.
6. Police blocked off the road and kept _____ away from the fire.
7. This court will free _____ and punish _____.
8. _____ can take strength from _____.

B. Student 1: ask a question. Use **the** and the adjective as the subject noun. Student 2: answer the question using the cues.

Ex. blind//Seeing Eye dogs
What do the blind need?
They need Seeing Eye dogs.

1. unemployed//jobs
2. poor//financial help
3. elderly//good medical treatment
4. overweight//exercise
5. hungry//food
6. sick//medicine
7. hard of hearing//hearing aids

C. Answer the questions with full sentences. Use an adjective from the list.

handicapped	impossible
rich	wounded
sick	poor

Ex. Who's that parking space for?
It's for the handicapped.

1. Who can afford to join that club?
2. Who do the paramedics help?
3. What did Don Quixote try to do?
4. Who did Florence Nightingale help?
5. Who did Robin Hood steal from?
6. Who did Robin Hood help?

8 Adjectives: Order of Modifying Adjectives

a **large, old, round, red** button
some **tall, straight, elegant** trees

A. Form noun phrases for each noun. Use three adjectives for each phrase.

Ex. birds
little, young, red birds

1. lamps
2. rooms
3. stones
4. flowers

Opinion	Size	Age	Shape	Color	Noun as adjective/Origin
pretty	big	old	flat	blue	leather
attractive	little	new	round	brown	wood
beautiful	large	young	square	gray	marble
plain	small		fat	green	crystal
homely	huge		thin	red	Spanish
	tiny		thick	white	

B. Fill in the blanks. Put the adjectives in parentheses in the most appropriate order.

1. He wore his **expensive new gray** jacket. (gray/new/expensive)
2. Tokuo drives an _____ _____ _____ Chevy. (blue/old/big)
3. I left my _____ _____ _____ briefcase on the train. (leather/brown/large)
4. It was a _____ _____ _____ meeting. (dull/pointless/long)
5. Our company is located in a _____ _____ _____ building. (office/modern/clean)
6. You'll find it in the _____ _____ _____ box. (rectangular/yellow/small)
7. There are _____ _____ _____ restaurants in the city. (inexpensive/good/Spanish)
8. My sister has _____ _____ _____ hair. (brown/curly/short)
9. Tom has a _____ _____ _____ face. (long/pale/thin)
10. My grandfather is a _____ _____ _____ man. (heavy/short/old)

C. Form noun phrases to describe the things in the pictures. Use two or three adjectives of your own choice in each noun phrase.

beautiful   tall
big   terrible
brave   ugly
comfortable   wild
little   wonderful
old

1. **a comfortable, big, old chair**

9 Relative Clauses: *that* Clause with Subject

the people (**that**) **I saw there**
the stuff (**that**) **they're burning**

A. Match 1–8 with a noun phrase from a–h and with a relative clause from s–z to form questions.
Use **that** with the relative clause.

1. Is that
2. Do you want
3. Why is this
4. How do you like
5. What happened on
6. Where can you get
7. Can you recognize
8. Are you talking about

a. the only information
b. the best toaster
c. a refrigerator
d. the packages
e. all the food
f. the garden
g. the days
h. the baskets

s. you can eat?
t. he gave her?
u. I was absent?
v. money can buy?
w. we worked on?
x. we sent by airmail?
y. Indians used for storage?
z. you don't have to defrost?

1. Is that the only information that he gave her?

B. Student 1: ask a **what** question about 1–9. Student 2: answer with **it's a** or **they're** and a noun phrase with a relative clause.

Ex. a one-way street
What's a one-way street?
It's a street that you can only go one direction on. (or) . . . that you can't go both ways on.

1. a raincoat
2. address books

3. a dictionary
4. photocopying machines
5. a wristwatch
6. a freezer
7. typing paper
8. life insurance policies
9. a drive-in bank window

C. Student 1: ask the question below using a selection from the chart. Student 2: answer using **the one** or **the ones** and a relative clause.

TVs	$352 19-inch color TV Remote control Cable ready	$200 Small black & white TV Four-inch screen Battery operated Completely portable	$689 25-inch color TV Remote control Stereo sound Oak cabinet case

Gloves	$12
	SPECIAL! TODAY ONLY
	Cotton work gloves
	Designed for heavy use
		$25
		Men's or women's driving
		  gloves
		Nylon and leather
			$80
			Men's or women's dress
			  gloves
			Black or brown kid

Cameras	$29.99 Instamatic camera Foolproof Built-in electronic flash	$155 35-mm instant camera Free case included Automatic focus Automatic film advance	$360 35-mm camera With 50-mm lens Zoom lens included Automatic film loading

Ex. If you went shopping today, which TV would you buy?
I'd buy the one that costs $200. (or) . . . the one that's completely portable.

10 Relative Clauses: *that* Clause without Subject

the people **that saw me**
the stuff **that's burning there**

A. Answer questions 1–10 with a noun modified by a **that** clause from a–j.

1. What evidence was destroyed?
2. What days are unbearable?
3. Which roads are slow?
4. What plants have long roots?
5. Which bank teller waited on you?
6. Which road is being patched?
7. What shoes are drying out?
8. Which company is in trouble?
9. Which doctor are they talking to?
10. What birds have long wings?

a. that go through the center of town
b. that performed the operation
c. that grow in the desert
d. that always waits on me
e. that are so hot and humid
f. that got wet on the porch
g. that proved his point
h. that glide long distances
i. that's losing money
j. that has holes in it

1. **The evidence that proved his point.**

B. Student 1: ask a yes/no question with a relative clause. Student 2: answer with **no** and a full sentence. Both: use the words in parentheses in the relative clauses.

Ex. Carmen likes boys. (smoke//don't smoke)
Does Carmen like boys that smoke?
No, she likes ones (boys) that don't smoke.

1. They found the car. (was used in the bank robbery//was used in the jewelry store robbery)
2. Westwood was the town. (lowered its property tax//lowered its school tax)
3. You will punish the kids. (played on the front lawn//ran through the flower garden)

4. Doris Clendening is the person. (handles your insurance policy//handles my travel arrangements)
5. He wants to marry a woman. (can hike 25 miles a day//can cook good spaghetti)
6. They bought the house. (had four bedrooms//had the big backyard)
7. José went to an optician. (graduated from George Washington University//studied in Europe)
8. My sister is seeing a young man. (works in her office//comes from Maine)
9. Meg Powell goes to stores. (have the cheapest prices//carry imported items)

C. Answer the questions with a noun modified by a relative clause.

1. What was a stegosaurus?
   A dinosaur that had plates on its back. (or)
   A reptile that lived a long time ago.
2. Who has he fallen in love with?
3. What does Ripley's Museum have?
4. What did Ichabod Crane see?

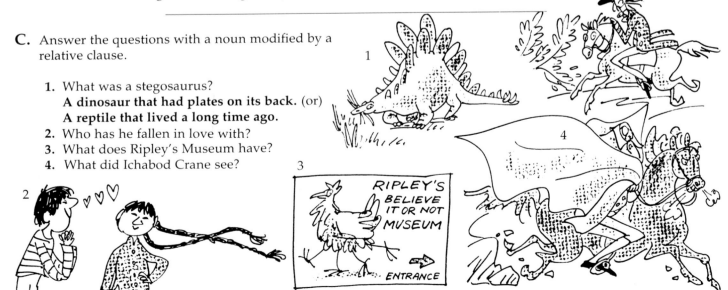

11 Relative Clauses: Nonrestrictive

my brother, **who serves in the navy**
those books, **which we had to read**

A. Complete sentences 1–10 with clauses a–j.

1. I bought a dictionary,
2. I have a can opener,
3. He got a used car,
4. Olga Zarges has a key chain,
5. Daryl has a good pair of shoes,
6. I want you to meet Jim Wonderly,
7. Janet cooked a marvelous dish,
8. She never saw her grandmother,
9. We took a picture of the museum,
10. I often play chess with my sister,

a. which he uses mostly for business
b. which is made of glass and stone
c. which he only wears to parties
d. which never works very well
e. which I need in my English class
f. who is a very good player
g. which has a "Z" on it
h. who owns the local newspaper
i. which she saw on TV
j. who died in 1952

1. **I bought a dictionary, which I need in my English class.**

B. Student 1: read the question. Student 2: answer with a full sentence. Choose one of the phrases in parentheses to form a sentence with the non-restrictive relative clause.

Ex. Who's this town named after? (my grandfather/ the man) who built the first building here in 1886
It's named after my grandfather, who built the first building here in 1886.

1. What's the tallest building in the world? (a Chicago skyscraper/the Sears Tower) which is 110 stories high

2. What battle ended Napoleon's career? (the Battle of Waterloo/a famous battle) which took place in 1815
3. When was she born? (on January 24/on the day) which turned out to be the coldest day of the winter
4. Who's going to rent this property? (a company/the Clover Company) which makes paint
5. Who was injured? (Marisol Martinez/the woman) who sells insurance
6. Who did your cousin Pat marry? (David Shepson/a young man) who is rapidly becoming a famous opera star
7. When did they get married? (in the year/in 1984) which was an important election year

C. Complete the sentences with a nonrestrictive relative clause.

1. We're going on Flight 285, **which leaves at 9:25.**
2. Have you heard of Neil Armstrong, _____?
3. We saw the giant redwoods, _____?
4. Did you read about the Chief Justice, _____?

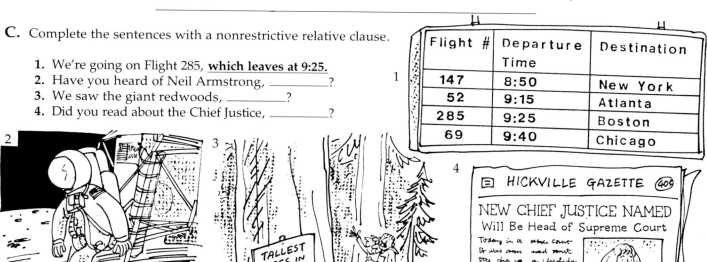

Flight #	Departure Time	Destination
147	8:50	New York
52	9:15	Atlanta
285	9:25	Boston
69	9:40	Chicago

TALLEST TREES IN THE WORLD

▣ HICKVILLE GAZETTE 40¢
NEW CHIEF JUSTICE NAMED
Will Be Head of Supreme Court

12 Relative Clauses: Restrictive vs. Nonrestrictive

my aunt, **who was born in 1950,**
a person **who was born in 1950**

A. Fill in the blanks using a clause from the box as restrictive (without commas) or nonrestrictive (with commas).

> which is black and white
> which needs technical aid
> who speak some French
> who'll be assigned to Africa

1. An animal **which is black and white** is easy to see in this terrain.
2. A zebra, _____, is hard to find in the brush.
3. Diplomats _____ should know some French.
4. These diplomats, _____, are all taking French courses.
5. Children _____ will study with Madame Levant in Room 219.
6. My children, _____, enjoyed themselves immensely in Quebec.
7. This U.N. agency supplies experts to any nation _____.
8. The United Nations sends experts to the country of Guiana, _____.

B. Complete the sentences with restrictive or nonrestrictive clauses by studying the family tree of Kathy Evans. The symbol (=) indicates married couples.

1. Frank and Anna Knapp had a daughter **who was born in 1934**.
2. Vernon Evans, _____, married Dorothy Knapp.
3. Kathy Evans's mother, _____, was born in 1934.
4. Bob Freschi, _____, was born in 1959.
5. Louise Richards, _____, married a man _____.
6. Louise Evans, _____, had a son _____.

Daniel Evans = Louise Richards	Frank Knapp = Anna Staso
1902–1977 b. 1908	1900–1983 1904–1985
mill worker housewife	salesman seamstress

Vernon Evans	=	Dorothy Knapp
b. 1932		b. 1934
insurance agent		real estate agent

Kathy Evans	=	Bob Freschi
b. 1958		b. 1959
advertising executive		insurance agent

C. Fill in the blanks in 1–10 with restrictive or nonrestrictive clauses from a–j.

1. I don't envy a person **who doesn't like music**.
2. Sally lost the necklace _____.
3. The lucky man _____ decided to keep his job at the clothing store
4. She bought a winter coat in the new store _____.
5. Thomas Edison _____ was born in 1847 in Milan, Ohio.
6. I work for the Star Company _____.
7. John Reynolds _____ could not be present to receive his award last night.
8. All the men _____ voted to go on strike for higher wages.
9. The Tams _____ are not thinking about getting married.
10. When they heard the police siren, the two men _____ escaped out the back door.

a. who worked in the assembly plant
b. who were divorced last year
c. who doesn't like music
d. who was voted best actor of the year
e. who invented the phonograph
f. which is the oldest toy manufacturing company in the United States
g. who were robbing the store
h. who won the two million dollar lottery last month
i. which was having an opening day sale
j. that Ted had given her for her birthday last week

13 Participial Phrase Modifiers: -ing Participles

a truck **hauling fresh fruit to market**
the passengers **leaning out of the windows**

A. Add modifying phrases a–j to the noun phrases in sentences 1–10.

1. She's looking for a job.
2. A car is much too expensive.
3. The baby almost tripped me.
4. Does she have any relatives?
5. Do you know that young woman?
6. Everybody must pay the admission.
7. She took a picture of some birds.
8. A policeman spoke to some children.
9. Why don't you throw away that bike?
10. I tried to get the attention of the waiter.

a. coming out of the elevator
b. not having a free ticket
c. paying about six dollars an hour
d. crawling on the floor
e. playing in the street
f. costing over $15,000
g. rusting in the yard
h. feeding their young
i. serving our table
j. living in Poland

1. **She's looking for a job paying about six dollars an hour.**

B. Answer the questions by matching noun phrases a–j with modifying phrases q–z.

1. What must Khalim eat?
2. What does Inez smell?
3. What did Mr. Vincent see?
4. Who can give us directions?
5. Who did you bring to the party?
6. What were you watching at the docks?
7. What's the letter carrier afraid of?
8. What does the satellite picture show?
9. What does Johnson have to read next?
10. What was on the front page of the paper?

a. that girl
b. those letters
c. the potatoes
d. a big storm
e. the big dog
f. an article
g. the ships
h. a light
i. anyone
j. food

q. growling at her
r. unloading cargo
s. shining in the sky
t. sitting on his desk
u. not containing salt
v. burning on the stove
w. forming out at sea
x. talking to the hostess
y. criticizing the Army
z. wearing a red armband

1. **Food not containing salt.**

C. Answer with a noun phrase. Use a modifying participle with the verb in parentheses.

1. What kind of truck turned over? (carry)
   A truck carrying chickens.
2. What kind of plant do they work at? (produce)
3. What kind of magazine is he reading? (tell about)
4. Who were they chasing? (hold)

14 Participial Phrase Modifiers: Past Participles

a truck **stopped in the middle of the road**
the ones **driven by older drivers**

A. Match the modifiers a–j with sentences 1–10.

1. French is a language.
2. Adrian's wrist hasn't healed yet.
3. Juanita carried the books home.
4. The math problems are wrong.
5. The tree had to be cut down.
6. They're putting tickets on the cars.
7. The thief entered through a gate.
8. Many books have colorful pictures.
9. Children have protein deficiencies.
10. Anne's credit cards haven't been returned.

  a. spoken by many people around the world
  b. not locked by the night guard
  c. raised on a vegetarian diet
  d. injured in the last game
  e. stolen from her purse
  f. intended for children
  g. struck by lightning
  h. parked on that side
  i. marked with a red x
  j. needed for her computer course

1. **French is a language spoken by many people around the world.**
2. **Adrian's wrist, injured in the last game, hasn't healed yet.**

B. First read this story.

This morning I witnessed an automobile accident. It happened so fast I could hardly believe it. A speeding truck rounded the corner and smashed into the side of a small passenger car, turning it over. The driver of the car was wedged under the steering wheel, unable to get loose. Her passenger lay bleeding on the ground. The truck remained upright and the driver staggered to the curb. It was terrible!

Within a matter of minutes, the police, a police ambulance, a fire truck, and another ambulance arrived. The firemen managed to free the woman still in the car while a member of the ambulance crew attended to the cuts on the head and legs of the woman lying on the ground. A doctor, who had appeared on the scene, examined both women and advised that they be taken to a hospital. The ambulance roared away. A policeman unsuccessfully tried to question the truck driver and then led him to the waiting police ambulance for treatment.

Within a few minutes, the street was clean. A policeman had swept away the broken glass; others had pushed the truck to the side of the road. A tow truck now on the scene hauled away the car, and the other cars left.

I stood there and looked around in amazement. It was as if nothing had ever happened!

Now complete the sentences that summarize what happened in the incident above. Fill in the blanks with appropriate past participles from the list.

break	cut	daze	demolish
hurt	injure	pin	throw

1. The firemen managed to free the woman **pinned** under the steering wheel.
2. The woman _____ from the car was attended to by a member of the ambulance crew. He applied first aid to her bleeding head and legs _____ by the broken glass.
3. A doctor examined both women _____ in the accident and said they could be moved.
4. In the meantime, a policeman unsuccessfully attempted to question the truck driver _____ in the accident.
5. The ambulance rushed the two women _____ in the crash to a nearby hospital.
6. A policeman swept away the glass from the headlights _____ in the crash.
7. The tow truck hauled away the car _____ by the impact.

17 Modals: had better and would rather

We **had better** (**not**) **eat** more.
Hadn't we **better eat** some more?

A. Form a sentence about each picture. Use **would rather . . . , but . . . had better . . . .**

1. **She'd rather go to school, but she'd better stay home.**

B. Form negative sentences like the example.

Ex. I/take the bus//use our car
I'd rather not take the bus, but I'd better.
I'd better not use our car.

1. Dan Stebbins/shovel the snow now//wait any longer
2. Connie/have the operation//worry about the cost
3. Tom/see the doctor yet//delay another day
4. Marie/quit smoking//ruin her health
5. Valerie Jones/eat breakfast today//go to work on an empty stomach
6. Kevin/wear hiking boots//wear sneakers on the hike
7. They/go to bed now//stay up until 2 a.m. again
8. My sister/follow the doctor's orders//eat any salty foods
9. Steve/talk to Ms. Stone//act without her advice

C. Student 1: ask an alternative yes/no question.
Student 2: answer with **I think . . . would rather . . . .**

Ex. Lois/play basketball/help in the garden
Does Lois want to play basketball, or would she rather help in the garden?
I think she'd rather play basketball.

1. the hikers/go on to the next station/camp here
2. your children/go swimming/play a video game
3. Greg/plan the family budget/talk on the phone
4. Luz/buy a new foreign car/keep her old car a while longer
5. Chuck/go on the picnic/stay home and watch the house
6. the taxi driver/pick up one more fare/quit work for the day
7. the Atlas Company/enlarge their factory/merge with Herculoids Inc.

18 Modals: Paraphrases of Modals

will/ would	= {	be going to be willing to	may/can = be allowed to	must = have to
can/could	=	be able to	might = be likely to	should = be good to

A. Answer the questions with **no, but** and a full sentence. Use the modals **can, could, will, would, may, might, must,** or **should.**

Ex. Are you able to box? (wrestle)
No, but I can wrestle.

1. Are they going to have fireworks tonight? (a carnival)
2. Is Ted allowed to go swimming now? (play volleyball)
3. Is it good to eat a lot of fatty food? (eat a lot of natural fibers)
4. Do the applicants have to hand in their forms now? (sign them)
5. Is the truck likely to break down? (get stuck)
6. Do you permit him to come early? (leave a little later)
7. Do you advise me to buy energy stocks? (invest in real estate)
8. Was the boy able to count to 100? (say the alphabet)
9. Are you going to enter the marathon? (enter the 5,000 meter race)

B. Fill in the blanks with **but** and a paraphrase in the past negative.

1. You should buy bonds now, **but it wasn't good to buy them last year**.
2. Edie may ride her bike on the street now, _____.
3. People must register their guns now, _____.
4. Marilyn can score 100,000 on the video game now, _____.
5. Ruth Chong will give her neighbor a ride now, _____.
6. Sam Cotten must go to a retirement home now, _____.
7. The children should go to camp now, _____.
8. The union might accept a wage cut now, _____.

C. Read the sentence. Then form a sentence using the words in parentheses and other words of your choice.

Ex. Jake has a flat tire. (will have to)
He'll have to change it. (or) **He'll have to get it fixed.** (or) **He'll have to take the bus.**

1. Miss Oller wants to work at the French Embassy. (must be able to)
2. We can't use this entrance. (will have to)
3. The customer doesn't have enough cash. (might be able to)
4. Mr. Hineman was in Colombia for four years. (should be able to)
5. We've already paid taxes on this income. (shouldn't have to)
6. Margie is only five years old. (shouldn't be allowed to)
7. Ruth has a date with Gordon tonight. (won't be able to)
8. Mr. Polson has just gotten over a bad cold. (might be dangerous for him to)
9. The Hickeys are going on a trip to Europe. (will be wise for them to)
10. The show has already started. (won't be possible for us to)

19 Modal Perfect with Future Meaning

She **will (won't) have graduated** by 1991.
Will (Won't) she **have graduated** by 1991?

A. Student 1: ask a **yes/no** question. Student 2: answer with a full sentence. Both: use **will have** or **won't have**.

Ex. Jack Lindsey/retire
Will Jack Lindsey have retired by 1990?
No, and he won't even have retired by 1995.
(or) **Yes, he will have retired by 1988.**

1. she/raise the children
2. Karen/finish her schooling
3. they/pay off their loan
4. interest rates/go down to five percent
5. space stations/become common
6. Pierre/learn English
7. Westwood/build the plantetarium
8. the highway department/complete the project
9. someone/find a cure for colds

B. Answer the questions with **not then** and a full sentence using the information in parentheses. Study the example.

Ex. Must Ms. Melleby have signed the travel request before tomorrow? (Friday)
Not then. But she must have signed it before Friday.

1. Must we have located Blanche before noon? (5 p.m.)
2. Can they have begun the operation before July? (August 15)
3. Should Mr. King have finished the monthly report before the first of the month? (the tenth of the month)
4. Must we have doubled our sales before January 1? (March 31)
5. Could Ed have passed the first-round test before March 10? (the end of March)
6. Should we have cleared this with Mr. Smith before the staff meeting? (the conference)
7. Should I have paid the tax before November? (the end of the year)
8. Must George have signed the permission form before Tuesday? (tomorrow)

C. Form question word questions. Use **will have** with the words given.

Ex. by/receive our message/they/when
When will they have received our message by?

1. it/been/since their first message/how long
2. by the end of your trip/travel/where/you
3. be on the road/by the end of your trip/how many days/you
4. by December 31/conduct/how many interviews/the reporter
5. by Friday/how much medicine/Mark/take
6. how tall/grow/Al/by the time we see him again
7. how long/Ruth/by the time she retires/work at this plant
8. learn about the machine/Alessandra/what/by the end of the training course
9. after two hours/cross the finish line/which runners

20 Modal Perfect with Past Meaning

She **might (not) have stayed** in Dallas.
Might (Mightn't) she have stayed in Dallas?

A. Answer with **yes** and a full sentence.

Ex. Was the water cold? (must)
Yes, it must have been cold.

1. Did the crew help the passengers into the lifeboats? (must)
2. Were worn brakes the cause of the accident? (may)
3. Did the army travel at night? (could)
4. Did Mr. Garrett enter the country at Boston? (might)
5. Did Rick get tired during the race? (must)
6. Did the doctor tell Mrs. Lopez to run two miles a day? (might)
7. Was Sharon on the swimming team? (could)

B. Form question word questions.

Ex. must/the storm/strike/when
When must the storm have struck?

1. could/hide her kittens/the cat/where
2. might/see the thief/who
3. a nurse/do in that situation/what/would
4. cause the power failure/may/what
5. could/see the other plane first/which/pilot
6. be in the oven/how long/should/this cake
7. could/how many matches/Nancy/win in 20 years
8. change their decision/should/the planning board/when
9. how/make such a mistake/the police officer/could

C. Read the sentence. Then form a sentence with the modal perfect negative using the words in parentheses.

Ex. Guy only got 55 on the math test. (must/study)
He must not have studied for it.

1. Jane can't find the file on Mr. Hockenberry. (must/file)
2. The department store repossessed the O'Briens' TV set. (must/make the payments)
3. Amin can't find his coat in the closet. (might/hang up)
4. Newkirk put forth his best effort in the match. (should/lose)
5. I don't know why I carried my wallet in my hip pocket. (might/lose)
6. Vernon lost the match to Westergren. (could/beat)
7. The typewriter is broken again. (could/fix)
8. Julie used to work for Mrs. Walker. (could/forget)

21 Modal Perfect with Conditional Meaning

I **would** (**wouldn't**) **have jumped.**
Would (**Wouldn't**) you **have jumped?**

A. Student 1: read the sentence. Student 2: ask **Would you have done that?** Student 1: answer with **no** and a full sentence.

Ex. Roy lost his watch, and he started to cry. (look for it)
Would you have done that?
No, I would have looked for it.

1. Edie found a book, and she kept it. (take it to the lost and found)
2. Greg Anderson's watch stopped, and he threw it away. (get it fixed)
3. The TV contestant missed the question about Mars. (know the answer)
4. My boss had to give a speech, and she had someone write it. (write it myself)
5. Betty McCulloch's cat had kittens, and she gave them away. (keep them)
6. He wasn't hungry, but he ate a big lunch. (just have a snack)
7. The speech was boring, but they sat through it. (leave the room)
8. The light was about to turn red, and she ran across the street. (wait for a green light)
9. The price was too high, but my uncle paid it. (complain to the manager)

B. Form sentences. Use two clauses with **shouldn't** and **should**.

Ex. eat/ice cream//fruit
He shouldn't have eaten the ice cream.
He should have eaten the fruit.

1. take/car//subway
2. bet/horse race//lottery
3. wear/sweater//parka
4. join/army//navy
5. write/novel//poetry

C. Student 1: form question word questions. Student 2: answer with a full sentence. Both: use **could have**, **should have**, or **might have**.

Ex. The Eagles didn't beat the Bulldogs. (who)
Who could they have beaten?
Well, they could have beaten the Lions. (or)
. . . anyone else.

1. Fidel lost his wallet yesterday. (where)
2. Juanita didn't buy "La Elegance" perfume. (what kind)
3. Ellen Tolley didn't go on the 8 a.m. plane. (when)
4. Jason Castle wasn't in his office. (where)
5. I didn't buy the Ford because I didn't have the money. (how much)
6. He didn't tell his family about the accident. (who)
7. She didn't try to win the baking contest. (what)
8. They didn't go to the right building. (where)
9. My aunt went to the emergency room yesterday. (what)

22 Modal Perfect Continuous

He **should (shouldn't) have been standing** there.
Should (Shouldn't) he have been standing there?

A. Respond with a negative sentence, and then an affirmative sentence using the word in parentheses. Study the example.

Ex. He was crying. (laugh)
He shouldn't have been crying. He should have been laughing.

1. She was buying gold. (silver)
2. The porters were working. (on vacation)
3. We were watching Carrie. (Marta)
4. Ms. Chilcote was standing. (lie down)
5. He was driving a sports car. (an economy car)
6. They were playing in the street. (on the sidewalk)
7. They were hiring more secretaries. (more drivers)
8. Mrs. Rose was burning the newspapers. (keep)
9. The company was reducing its advertising. (increase)

B. Form a sentence with the modal perfect continuous to follow 1–8. Use the information from a–h.

1. Donald's all wet.
2. Her teeth are bad.
3. Nobody saw the thief.
4. Her telephone was busy.
5. They looked very unhappy.
6. He was waiting on the porch.
7. They were all out of breath.
8. A truck was stopped over there.

a. should/wait inside
b. could/wear a disguise
c. might/deliver furniture
d. might/have an argument
e. might/try to call us
f. must/eat a lot of candy
g. must/run hard
h. must/walk in the rain

1. **He must have been walking in the rain.**

C. Student 1: ask a yes/no question about each picture. Use **will** and the time expressions. Student 2: give a short answer.

1. at noon/two hours
   At noon will they have been operating for two hours?
   Yes, they will have.
2. in 1990/40 years
3. on Tuesday/ten weeks
4. by 9:30/half an hour

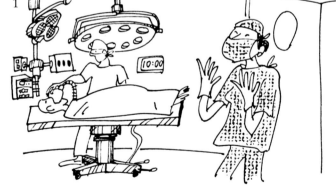

2

NAME: Bill Lanton
ADDRESS: 299 Walnut Avenue, Bloomtown, IN
AGE: 57
DATE HIRED: 2/16/50
TEL.#: 344-1696
COMMENTS: Very faithful and reliable. Accepts responsibility for tasks.

3
Spaceship Intrepid Tuesday (Tenth Week)

4

BOXING TONIGHT 9:15
JOE LOUISIANA VS. ALI BASHER

23 Modal Perfect Passive

She **could (couldn't) have been elected** last year.
Could (Couldn't) she have been elected last year?

A. Form a negative sentence to follow 1–9. Use the information in parentheses.

> **Ex.** The water wasn't safe to drink. (must/boil)
> **It must not have been boiled.**

1. Robert isn't well behaved. (must/discipline)
2. Alicia didn't know about the sale. (must/tell)
3. The children are very hungry already. (might/feed)
4. That report isn't accurate. (might/check over)
5. Mr. Lopez didn't fall far. (might/injure badly)
6. The electric bill is past due. (could/pay)
7. Ms. Wilson's hair was straight. (could/curl)
8. The radio still doesn't work. (can/fix)
9. The furnace filter is terribly dirty. (can/change recently)

B. Student 1: ask a yes/no question about each sentence. Use **should**.
Student 2: answer with **no** and a full sentence using the words in parentheses.

> **Ex.** Dr. McGarvey was told today. (much earlier)
> **Should he have been told today?**
> **No, he should have been told much earlier.**

1. The plants were set two feet apart. (four feet apart)
2. The bills were paid yesterday. (last week)
3. Gary was fired last week. (last year)
4. The replacement parts were ordered recently. (a long time ago)
5. The garage door was painted. (repair first)
6. The lawn was watered. (cut first)
7. Helene's arm was treated. (X-ray first)
8. The baby was fed. (bathe first)
9. The book was put on the library shelves. (catalog first)

C. Student 1: ask a question with **how many**. Use **will** and **the year 2000**. Student 2: answer with a phrase or sentence.

1. marry
   How many years will they have been married in the year 2000?
   Twenty-four. (or) They'll have been married 24 years.
2. fly
3. serve
4. earn

1

Rutherford County   No. 024063
Office of the County Clerk
Marriage License Bureau
Certificate of Marriage Registration

This is to certify that Harold James McDaniel residing at
915 Cherry Lane, Millville born February 12, 1950
and Martha Elizabeth Chichester residing at 241 Maple
Avenue, Apt. 4B, Millville born May 21, 1952
Were Married
on   October 8, 1976 at Millville.   *Richard Michaels*
Certified on November 10, 1976   RICHARD MICHAELS
                                           COUNTY CLERK

2

MAJESTIC AIRLINES

Annual Report   Chart 47

Expected number of miles flown:

1990	3 million
2000	31 million
2010	40 million

3

Harry's Happy Hamburgers

Annual predicted sales
Projected sales

1990	20 million burgers sold
2000	34 million burgers sold
2010	46 million burgers sold

4

First National Savings Bank

Sample of interest earned with First National:

If you bought a certificate of deposit for $1,000 with us in 1980 (at 17% annual interest), by 1990 you'd have $2,700, by 2000 $4,400!

So come join our savings family!

24 Present Perfect Continuous: Statements

I **have been studying**.
I **haven't been writing** letters.

A. Form negative and affirmative sentences. Study the example.

> **Ex.** The guard/watch the door//sleep
> **The guard hasn't been watching the door.**
> **He's been sleeping.**

1. Tom/work hard//take it easy
2. Teresa/cut hair//give shampoos
3. Ari and Peggy/watch the movie//eat popcorn
4. The company/use the old brushes//throw them away
5. The judge/listen to the witness//write something
6. His wife/save money for the future//buy lottery tickets
7. The cat/hunt mice//sleep on the sofa
8. Jerry/cook the steaks//play horseshoes
9. Those artists/paint pictures//sit around
10. Keith/work overtime//go home early

B. Form sentences. Use the contractions 's or 've if possible.

> **Ex.** Beth/knit a sweater//I
> **Beth's been knitting a sweater, and I have too.**

1. Paul/play in the mud//Mike
2. Amin/lose support// his partner
3. She/keep a secret//he
4. We/borrow money// the Finches
5. Juan/buy Safeco stock//Maggie
6. They/hire engineers//we
7. Our doctor/ charge more// our dentist
8. Ed/use language tapes//Valerie
9. You/work hard// your husband

C. Form a sentence about the people in each picture. Use the present perfect continuous tense.

1. Jose/Lisa
   Jose has been fishing, and Lisa has been swimming.
2. Henry/Maria
3. Mr. Ramos/Mercedes
4. Patty/Mark

25 Present Perfect Continuous: Questions

Has (Hasn't) she **been looking?**
How long **has** she **been looking?**

A. Student 1: ask a question word question.
Student 2: reply in the present continuous tense.
Student 1: ask another question word question.
Student 2: reply using the cue.

Ex. Joyce//do research//how long//three or four
months
What's Joyce been doing recently?
She's been doing research.
How long has she been doing that?
For three or four months.

1. Mr. Garcia//work in Chicago//how long//several
months

2. Henry//work at the King Automobile Factory//
how long//since last year
3. Dr. Ferguson//attend some conferences//where//in
Brazil and France
4. Heather//look for a new job//why//she doesn't like
what she's doing now
5. Abdul//study creative writing//why//he wants to be
a journalist
6. Nadia//study in Paris//what//French literature
7. Dr. Nelson//study Chinese//why//he has been
asked to lecture in Beijing
8. your mother//write a novel//how long//five or six
years

B. Form sentences about the King Automobile Company. Use the verb **rise** or **fall**.

	Production (No. of Cars)	Work Force (No. of Workers)	Sales (In thousands)	Debt (In thousands)
1960	15,000	3,800	$650	$1,800
1970	19,500	3,500	$2,300	$2,500
1980	22,000	2,900	$5,100	$1,400
1985	25,000	2,440	$8,800	$970

Ex. Automobile production has been rising.

C. Fill in the blanks with the present perfect continuous tense of one of the verbs and a tag question.

not appear
bark
bring
broadcast
change
date
not drink
not earn
fall
not make
not melt
run

1. The snow**'s been falling** hard, **hasn't** it?
2. Tina _____ Jason, _____ she?
3. The company _____ money, _____ it?
4. Those dogs _____ a lot, _____ they?
5. Your watch _____ slow, _____ it?
6. The leaves _____ color, _____ they?
7. The baby _____ much milk, _____ he?
8. The weatherman _____ accurate predictions, _____ he?
9. The ice _____ on the lake, _____ it?
10. The boss _____ a bag lunch to work, _____ she?
11. Radio stations _____ a lot of election news, _____ they?
12. The Santini Sisters _____ in concerts, _____ they?

26 Present Perfect Continuous: Compared with Present Perfect

I've been saving money.
You've already saved enough.

A. Answer the questions with **no** and a full sentence. Use the present perfect continuous tense and the present perfect tense as in the example.

> **Ex.** Have you started the report? (think about it/ some time)
> **No, I've been thinking about it for some time, but I haven't started it yet.**

1. Has she finished her report? (work on it/several days)
2. Have you sent in your taxes? (work on them/ over a week)
3. Has Nancy found her ring? (look for it/several days)
4. Have George and his wife gone to London? (plan that trip/a year)
5. Has Luis returned the library book? (plan to do it/two weeks)
6. Have the Parks sold their house? (advertise it/ six months)
7. Has Tommy caught any fish? (fish/three or four hours)
8. Have the Rockets won many hockey games? (play/two and a half months)
9. Has Mr. Bond hired Mrs. Scott? (consider her/a while)
10. Have you painted the bedroom? (get ready to do it/a week)
11. Has Linda subscribed to the newspaper? (buy newsstand copies/a year)
12. Has Brad found a new job? (look for one/two months)

B. Fill in the blanks with the present perfect tense or present perfect continuous tense of a verb from the list.

blow	call	go	not joke	not rain
build	cost	happen	know	never see
snow	not write	shop	watch	

1. Of course I'm going to buy an airplane! I **haven't been joking** with you.
2. Linda isn't here. She _____ at department stores all day.
3. Melanie's very excited. She _____ the ocean before.
4. The ground's all white. It _____ all morning.
5. It's awfully dry. It _____ in six weeks.
6. Freddie's an old friend. I _____ him for 20 years.
7. No one answers the phone. I _____ for more than an hour.
8. The wind's certainly strong. It _____ down some big branches.
9. There's loud music in Helen's room. She _____ her book report.
10. Diego's trying to fix the radio. He _____ to the store for a part.
11. They _____ that skyscraper for more than two years. So far, it _____ 150 million dollars.
12. That police car is still across the street. I _____ it for an hour, but nothing _____ yet.

27 Past Perfect

I enjoyed the trip to Greece because I **hadn't been** there before.
Hadn't you **gone** there in 1980?

A. Answer the questions with **no** and a full sentence. Use the past perfect tense and **already**.

Ex. Did the nurse give you some aspirin for your headache? (I/take)
No, I'd already taken some.

1. Did you have lunch with Henry? (he/eat)
2. Did you get that good used car? (the dealer/sell)
3. Did Jeffrey catch the bus? (it/leave)
4. Did you tell Mr. Forbes about his mistakes? (he/correct)
5. Did Tom and Nancy get to school on time? (the bell/ring)
6. Did Romesh change his order? (the chef/cook)
7. Did Mrs. Yung bid on the painting? (someone/buy)
8. Could the teacher change the mark? (he/report)
9. Could Melissa get into her dorm? (they/lock the door)

B. Ask a negative question. Use the past perfect tense, **ever**, and **before**.

Ex. I met June Snow last Sunday.
Hadn't you ever met her before?

1. Ted bet on a race horse last week for the first time.
2. Judy drove my new car last Saturday.
3. Ms. Sellers sang her first solo last Sunday.
4. I read Hemingway's *The Old Man and the Sea* last night.
5. We saw *Star Wars* last week.
6. I tasted Tom's chocolate cake at the party.
7. I heard Michael Jackson's latest album last week.
8. Mary wore her new sweater to the picnic.
9. They tried the steak at the Royal Pub yesterday.

C. Fill in the blanks to complete the sentences. Form affirmative and negative sentences about the lives of the Wiley children. Use the past perfect tense and **already** or **yet**.

Rudy	Sarah	Patrick
1934 Born	1936 Born	1945 Born
1952 Graduated from high school	1954 Graduated from high school	1963 Graduated from high school
1953 Joined Army	1958 Graduated from college	1969 College degree (M.S.)
1957 Sergeant	1958 Married	1969 Reporter on *News*
1966 To Vietnam	1960 Worked at Murphy's	1970 Reporter in Vietnam
1973 Married	1961 Maternity leave	1974 Local editor
1978 Colonel	1976 Manager at Loft's	1981 Published book

1. When Patrick graduated from high school,
   Rudy had not yet gone to Vietnam.
2. When Sarah graduated from college, _____.
3. When Rudy went to Vietnam, _____.
4. When Patrick became a reporter on the *News*, _____.
5. When Sara got married, _____.
6. When Patrick published his book, _____.

28 Past Perfect Continuous

Had she **been parking** in the street?
She **had (not) been parking** in the driveway.

A. Fill in the blanks with the past perfect continuous tense of a verb from the list. Use the contraction **'d** if possible.

not attract	invest	not lock
bother	not turn in	give
play	not earn	eat
burn		

1. The boys' mouths were all blue. They**'d been eating** blueberries.
2. The company went out of business. They _____ money for a year.
3. A thief broke into our office. I _____ the door.
4. He got rid of that old car. It _____ him trouble for some time.
5. Ben changed to the trumpet. He _____ the French horn.
6. The play closed after six weeks. It _____ many people.
7. Our neighbor died suddenly. He left his family a lot of money. He _____ in valuable stocks.
8. They finally put out the forest fire. It _____ for over a week.
9. Marge dropped her accounting course. She _____ any assignments.
10. He had to get glasses. His eyes _____ him.

B. Read the paragraph about Brian Dunn. Student 1: ask eight questions about Brian's training before the meet. Student 2: give a short **yes** or **no** answer. Study the example.

Brian Dunn wanted to be a running champion. He trained very hard every day. He got up at 5:30 and ran for half an hour. Then he had a light breakfast. Every morning he did many leg and breathing exercises. He circled the track 30 times every morning and afternoon. He wore heavy shoes part of the time. He didn't drink milk before or after running, but he ate a couple of small candy bars. He got exactly eight hours' sleep. Finally, his hard work paid off. He won the City Running Championship meet in the fall of 1978.

Ex. Had Brian been training every day before the meet?
Yes, he had.

C. Student 1: ask a question word question about each picture. Student 2: answer with a full sentence.

1. what
   What had the child been drawing on the wall?
   He'd been drawing a picture of a train.
2. where
3. what
4. how long

29 Summary of Past and Perfect Tenses

See summary table of past and perfect tenses
on the inside back cover.

A. Fill in the blanks with the past tense, the past
continuous tense, or a perfect tense of the verbs in
parentheses.

1. I know John's father. I ___**met**___ him last
   week. (meet)
2. Peter had to climb through a window. He
   _____ his house key. (lose)
3. Yuri's mother yelled at him. He _____ his
   food at his brother. (throw)
4. Her back hurts a lot. She _____ over in the
   garden. (bend)
5. He finally went to the dentist last Friday. His
   tooth _____ for two weeks. (ache)
6. I'm going to call the repairman. I _____
   trouble with my typewriter. (have)

7. We watched the ants. They _____ food into
   their tunnels. (carry)
8. I'm waiting for next week's check. I _____
   already _____ this week's. (spend)
9. My friend scared me. I _____ a mystery story,
   and he _____ sharply on my window. (read,
   knock)
10. We saw Mt. Shasta last summer, but we _____
    not _____ Mt. Lassen. We _____ never
    _____ Mt. Lassen. (see)
11. I want to read *The Adventures of Tom Sawyer*. I
    _____ never _____ it. (read)
12. Lin wanted to play a video game. He _____
    never _____ one. He _____ one called
    "Space Dust." He _____ it several times since
    then. (play)

B. Answer the questions with full sentences. Use a perfect tense. Study the picture.

1. What has the young boy with the musical instrument been doing?
   He's been taking a music lesson.
2. What fruit has the woman bought?
3. Has the produce man been selling fruits or vegetables?
4. What has the man in front of Fuller's Menswear just done?
5. What has he been drinking?
6. What has the woman in the upstairs window been doing?

30 Passive: Present and Past Statements

is (isn't) seen   was (wasn't) seen
are (aren't) seen   were (weren't) seen
am (am not) seen

A. Form a complete sentence from each headline. Use the date in the sentence.

November 22, 1963 President Kennedy Killed in Dallas	*December 3, 1984* **Thousands Hurt in Bhopal, India** **Chemical Accident**
July 17, 1969 **Apollo 11 Moon Rocket Launched**	*September 19, 1985* Mexico City Hit by Major Earthquake
July 4, 1976 Bicentennial Celebrated Across Country	*November 19, 1985* U.S.–U.S.S.R. Summit Opened in Geneva
August 3, 1981 Airlines Struck by Air Traffic Controllers	*January 28, 1986* **Seven Astronauts Killed in *Challenger* Explosion**
November 6, 1984 Reagan Re-elected by a Landslide	*May 5, 1986* New Lows Reached for Oil Prices

Ex. President Kennedy was killed in Dallas on November 22, 1963.

_____

B. Student 1: form a sentence beginning with **why**.
Student 2: reply with a passive sentence using the cue phrases.

Ex. bake these potatoes//fry these potatoes
Why did they bake these potatoes?
They weren't baked; they were fried.

1. wash this floor//sweep this floor
2. shoot the beavers//trap the beavers
3. keep old newspapers//throw old newspapers away
4. slice the apples at the cannery//peel the apples at the cannery
5. spend all their money on clothes//invest all their money in stocks
6. cancel today's game//postpone today's game
7. throw out the sour milk//use the sour milk in cooking
8. type those formal invitations//write the formal invitations by hand
9. take the case to court//settle the case out of court
10. throw away all the old books//sell all the old books

_____

C. Fill in the blanks to complete an affirmative sentence, and then form a negative sentence. Use a verb from the list.

bake   break   hit   pay   raise   shoot   steal   take

1. The thief **was shot** in the arm. (in the back)
   He wasn't shot in the back.
2. The thief _____ to the hospital. (to jail)
3. The jewelry _____ on Sunday. (on Monday)
4. Those windows _____ by rocks. (by hail)
5. This bread _____ this morning. (yesterday)
6. The pedestrian _____ by a motorcycle. (by a car)
7. The flag _____ at 7 a.m. (at 8 a.m.)
8. We _____ on February 19. (on February 26)

31 Passive: Use of Active vs. Passive

They **mailed** the packages.
The packages **were mailed**.

A. Form an active and a passive sentence. Study the example.

Ex. 1455/Johann Gutenberg/first printed book/ produce
In 1455, Johann Gutenberg produced the first printed book.
The first printed book was produced by Johann Gutenberg in 1455.

1. 1610/Galileo/Jupiter's four largest moons/ discover
2. 1648/Shah Jehan/Taj Mahal/finish
3. 1774/Joseph Priestly/oxygen/discover
4. 1808/Beethoven/his Fifth Symphony/complete
5. 1814/Francis Scott Key/"The Star Spangled Banner"/write
6. 1823/Clement Moore/"Visit from St. Nicholas"/ write
7. 1863/Abraham Lincoln/Emancipation Proclamation/sign
8. 1867/United States/Alaska from Russia/buy
9. 1872/Thomas Adams/chewing gum/invent
10. 1875/Bizet/*Carmen*/complete
11. 1903/the Wright brothers/first airplane flight/ make
12. 1905/Albert Einstein/theory of relativity/ formulate
13. 1935/Carl McGee/parking meter/invent
14. 1949/George Orwell/the novel *Nineteen Eighty-Four*/write
15. 1954/Roger Bannister/first four-minute mile/run
16. 1964/Nobel prize committee/peace prize to Martin Luther King/award
17. 1967/Dr. Christiaan Barnard/first human heart transplant/perform
18. 1982/Italy/World Cup in soccer/win

B. Fill in the blanks with active or passive verb phrases. Use verbs from the list.

get	invite	move	read	send
build	have	like	postpone	see
spend	tie up	visit		

Ted: Hi, Jody! Where have you been?
Jody: Oh, hi! I **was sent** to New York on business last week.
Ted: Great! I _____ New York very much. We _____ a week there in 1980. We _____ by a friend of my wife's. Did you _____ any free time? Did you _____ anything new?

Jody: Well, I _____ some free time. There was a very bad snowstorm one day. Traffic _____ for hours. Nothing could _____, and the day's meeting _____. Luckily, my hotel was just across the street from the Metropolitan Museum of Art and I _____ the Chinese courtyard there.
Ted: Oh, I _____ about that. It _____ inside the museum by Chinese artisans.
Jody: That's right. The courtyard was beautiful and very restful.

32 Passive: Present and Past Yes/No Questions

Are bicycles **made** in Japan?   Yes, they **are**.
Was that bicycle **made** in Japan?   No, it **wasn't**.

A. Student 1: read each sentence. Student 2: ask a passive yes/no question. Use the information in parentheses. Student 1: give a short **yes** or **no** answer.

Ex. They pay the employees on Fridays. (every Friday)
Are the employees paid every Friday?
Yes, they are.

1. They count the cash in the back room. (the front window)

2. They wash the buses on Saturdays. (every week)
3. They invest money in stocks. (in real estate)
4. They grow corn and wheat in the Midwest. (grain)
5. They manufacture automobiles in this factory. (passenger cars)
6. They sell 15 cars every week. (30 cars)
7. They ring the church bells on Sunday. (on Saturday)
8. They admit people free on Tuesdays and Thursdays. (children)
9. They invite tourists to the castle on weekends. (to the fort)

B. Student 1: ask a passive yes/no question about each picture. Use the past tense. Student 2: answer the question with **no** and a full sentence.

1. elect/by 1,000,000 votes
   Was Richards elected by a million votes?
   No, he was elected by 2,000 votes.

2. dig/by hand
3. attend/by a lot of people
4. paint/with a roller

C. Answer the question with **no** and a passive sentence.

Ex. Aren't diamonds found in Minnesota? (South Africa)
No, they're found in South Africa.

1. Wasn't the phone installed on Friday? (yesterday)
2. Weren't the chairs delivered to Maple Street? (the wrong address)
3. Isn't the money kept in a safe? (the bottom drawer)
4. Wasn't that sweater knit by your mother? (my grandmother)
5. Weren't the chickens fed this morning? (at noon)
6. Wasn't Rinaldo hit by a rock? (a snowball)
7. Aren't color TVs sold here? (at our other store)
8. Wasn't all the money spent on one building? (several buildings)
9. Weren't psychology and philosophy taught last year? (two years ago)

33 Passive: Present and Past Question Word Questions

Where/When **was** the stranger **seen**?
Who/What **was seen** in the water?

A. Ask a passive **who** question. Use the preposition **by**.

Ex. A thief was caught in a warehouse.
   Who was he caught by?

1. These chairs were made 150 years ago.
2. Juan was hired for the new position.
3. Some important papers were burned.
4. The child was saved from the river.
5. The Whites were finally given a loan.
6. The poem was written in 1822.
7. The chickens were fed this noon.
8. The audience was amused.

B. Read each sentence. Then ask a **where** or a **when** question. Use the passive voice.

Ex. We ordered the sweaters in May. (the shirts)
   When were the shirts ordered?

1. They collect old newspapers at the *Times* Building. (aluminum cans)
2. I checked the oil last week. (the brakes)
3. They started the art program last October. (the music program)
4. They made the plane reservations last week. (the hotel reservations)
5. They sold the diamonds in Australia. (the emeralds)
6. They found one hiker in a mountain cave. (the other)
7. They painted the outside of the house last summer. (the inside)
8. They feed the elephants in the morning. (monkeys)

C. Form passive sentences about the book. Study the example.

Published by Oxford University Press. Cover design by Akiko Pei. Illustrations by Fred Wilson. First printing: July 1987 Printed in the United States of America.	**The Habits of Quails** by *Jeremy Harben* 1987 Oxford University Press

Ex. **The book was published by Oxford University Press.**

34 Passive: Present and Past Continuous

is (isn't) being checked   was (wasn't) being checked
are (aren't) being checked   were (weren't) being checked
am (am not) being checked

A. Read each sentence. Then match them with items a–h and form a negative passive sentence.

1. The old TV set is being fixed.
2. The applicants are being tested.
3. Her letters are being forwarded to her.
4. The meat's being broiled.
5. He's being warned.
6. The actor was being introduced.
7. The vegetables were being given away.
8. The new student was being given attention.

a. arrested
b. fried
c. hired yet
d. ignored
e. interviewed
f. left in the mailbox
g. sold
h. traded in

1. **It isn't being traded in.**

B. Student 1: ask a passive yes/no question. Student 2:
answer the questions with **no** and a full sentence.

1. feed
   Is the baby being fed?
   No, he's being changed.
2. cut
3. wash

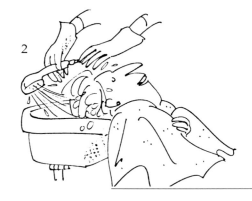

C. Read each sentence. Student 1: ask a passive
yes/no question. Student 2: give a short **yes**
answer. Student 1: ask a **who** question. Student 2:
answer.

Ex. David was teasing Betty.
   Was Betty being teased?
   Yes, she was.
   Who was she being teased by?
   (She was being teased) By David.

1. The Fargo Construction Company was building
   a new office.

2. The fans are photographing the winning horse.
3. Mr. Trapp is replacing the dead batteries.
4. The election committee is counting the votes.
5. The Milo Foundation was financing the art
   exhibit.
6. The senator was entertaining foreign newspaper
   reporters.
7. Some truck drivers are opposing the new union.
8. The Department of Parks is constructing a soccer
   field there.
9. A small group of taxpayers were planning a
   protest.

35 Passive with Indirect Objects

Was **John** given a watch?
He was given a clock.
Who was given a watch?

A. Fill in the blanks with a subject pronoun and a passive verb phrase (a form of **be** plus a past participle).

1. We asked for a catalog, but **we were sent** application forms. (send)
2. He didn't get a raise, but _____ one. (promise)
3. She wants another piece of candy, but _____ to eat any more. (not allow)
4. I didn't have to buy a wallet. _____ one. (give)
5. The children didn't know the safety rules because _____ them. (not teach)
6. I wanted to be manager, but _____ the job. (not offer)
7. She couldn't manage all of her packages. _____ by a neighbor. (help)
8. She's the sales manager now. _____ a promotion last month. (give)
9. We ordered 5 boxes, but _____ 50. (send)
10. He didn't know about the security problems. _____ about the recent robberies. (not tell)

B. Read each active sentence. Then form a passive sentence with the new information.

Ex. The company pays the clerks $150 a week. (the manager/$200)
The manager is paid $200 a week.

1. They billed the Sanchezes $75. (the Joneses/ $95)
2. Someone sent Lois a nasty letter. (Oliver/a nice birthday card)
3. They trained Doris in computer programming. (Ling/in proofreading)
4. We show ordinary visitors the assembly line. (scientists/the research labs)
5. The master of ceremonies gives the contestant a clue. (the audience/the answer)
6. We read the younger children fairy tales. (the older children/mystery stories)
7. They told his wife the truth. (his mother/ another story)
8. They made the dessert yesterday. (the entree/ this morning)
9. They ship most things by rail. (perishable items/by air)
10. We typeset the body of the book first. (the index/last)

C. Describe what is happening to the animals in the picture. Study the example.

1. bamboo
   The panda is being fed bamboo.
2. peanuts
3. meat
4. fish
5. bananas
6. leaves

36 Passive: Present Perfect and Past Perfect

has (hasn't) been taken
have (haven't) been taken
had (hadn't) been taken

A. Form passive question word questions.

   Ex. been/by/has/hired/Marisol/who
     Who has Marisol been hired by?

    1. been/has/out of/pulled/the magician's hat/what
    2. been/by/has/interviewed/Phil/who
    3. been/found/have/his fingerprints/where
    4. been/has/how/learned/the name of the winner
    5. been/had/invented/that tool/when
    6. been/by/checked/had/the men/which doctors
    7. been/have/how long/these products/used

B. Read each sentence. Then form an affirmative or a negative passive sentence. Use the present or past perfect tense.

   Ex. Kim's sick. (take to the hospital)
     He has been taken to the hospital.

    1. Mr. Jones disappeared the day before yesterday. (kidnap)
    2. I'll be late to the office. (delay this morning)
    3. The weapons were recovered. (hide in a cave)
    4. Madeline will go to Yale in the fall. (give a scholarship there)
    5. The old oak tree fell. (weaken on the inside)
    6. The jewelry was missing. (steal)
    7. My ring was right in my pocket. (steal)
    8. We aren't going to the party. (invite)

C. Student 1: ask **yes/no** questions about items on this automobile repair order. Student 2: give short answers.

   Ex. Has the engine oil been changed yet?
     Yes, it has.

Schlagel's Garage

Repair Order No. 19534

Check	Service	Cost
✓	Change engine oil	$9.50
✓	Change oil filter	8.85
	Adjust drive belts	
✓	Check timing	12.00
	Replace spark plugs	
	Rotate tires	
	Install new muffler	
		TOTAL

37 Passive: Modals

It **will (won't) be checked** today.
Will (Won't) it **be checked** today?
What **will (won't) be checked** today?

A. Read each sentence. Then form another sentence. Use **but** and the information in parentheses.

> **Ex.** They won't search his room. (his suitcase)
> **His room won't be searched but his suitcase will (be).**

1. He won't pay his electric bill this week. (his phone bill)
2. You can't force this lock. (that lock)
3. They can refund a first-class ticket. (an economy-class ticket)
4. They should reduce the sales tax. (the gasoline tax)
5. They shouldn't retire Professor Gross. (Professor Sawyer)
6. It would damage the ceiling. (the walls)
7. They will cancel the hockey game. (the ski jumping contest)
8. They might find the stolen money. (the robbers)
9. They will invite the governor. (the president)
10. They won't send the mirrors by truck. (the chairs)
11. You shouldn't drink this wine right away. (this milk)

B. Student 1: read the sentence. Student 2: ask a yes/no question. Student 1: give a short **yes** or **no** answer.

> **Ex.** You should walk the dog. (this afternoon)
> **Should he be walked this afternoon?**
> **Yes, he should (be).**

1. She should bandage her foot. (with a cloth)
2. They will send her father to prison. (soon)
3. We can finish the painting job. (before dark)
4. They'll send up a spaceship. (to Mars)
5. He can turn out the lights. (now)
6. They can take enough food. (in the car)
7. Someone will solve the mystery. (by a child)

C. Student 1: ask passive question word questions about each picture. Student 2: give short answers.

1. interview
   Who will be interviewed first?
   Jackson will (be).
2. wash
3. choose
4. remove

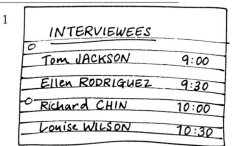

38 Infinitive or Gerund: Negative

He managed **not to forget** the date.
She considered **not wearing** her glasses.

A. Read each sentence. Then form another sentence. Use a negative infinitive or gerund.

   Ex. Our parents are sleeping. (promise/make noise)
   We've promised not to make noise.

1. Mr. Fong's getting a little better. (practice/use a cane)
2. I'm changing my major. (decide/take any more physics courses)
3. You don't drink enough orange juice. (risk/get enough vitamin C)
4. Paul got up early this morning. (manage/wake up his wife)
5. Children like summer vacation. (enjoy/study every day)
6. Postage has gone up again. (consider/send Christmas cards this year)
7. The students are typing fast. (learn/look at the keyboard)
8. I'll let you go downtown. (promise/spend more than $15)
9. I'm sorry my best friend moved away. (miss/see her every day)

B. Student 1: ask a yes/no question. Student 2: answer with **no** and a full sentence. Use a negative infinitive or gerund.

   Ex. he seems/be angry
   Does he seem to be angry?
   No, he seems not to be angry.

1. she pretended/be a student
2. they decided/use the elevator
3. I suggest/take an extra suitcase
4. they agreed/share expenses
5. you expect/stay long
6. he manage/eat much salt
7. they've discussed/send her to camp
8. she enjoys/wear shoes in summer
9. the company considered/increase prices

C. Answer the questions with a full sentence. Use a negative infinitive or gerund.

1. What do they hate?
They hate not finding a seat. (or) **. . . not being able to sit.**
2. What's she hoping?
3. What did they agree?
4. What does he enjoy?

39 Infinitive or Gerund: Perfect

to have saved
having saved

A. Fill in the blanks with the perfect gerund form of a verb from the list.

break	fool	lose	take	win
fall	invite	see	tell	work

1. Jan later laughed about **having fallen** into the pond.
2. Howard is sure of _____ an unidentified flying object in the sky once.
3. We were very disappointed at _____ the championship game.
4. The little girl cried over _____ her doll's arm.
5. He didn't lie about _____ for a computer company.
6. The children were laughing at _____ their parents.
7. I'm sorry about _____ Mr. Gonzalez about your financial difficulties.
8. The suspect finally admitted to _____ Mrs. Thornhill's jewelry.
9. Martin Luther King is famous for _____ the Nobel Peace Prize.
10. Have you forgotten about _____ your husband to lunch?

B. Student 1: ask a yes/no question. Use a perfect tense infinitive or gerund. Student 2: answer with **no** and a full sentence.

Ex. you plan/save $5,000 by next year//save $7,500
Do you plan to have saved $5,000 by next year?
No, I just plan to have saved $7,500.

1. he want/do something famous before his death//raise his children
2. Frank promised/put in a new transmission before 5//change the filter
3. the author expects/finish his book by January 1// write part of it
4. Mr. McNamara pretended/write the book// read it
5. the student admitted/copy his neighbor's test// not study for the test
6. the player remembers/leave the game//score the winning goal
7. she mentioned/grow up in Wisconsin//go to college there
8. your daughter hopes/earn her medical degree by next year/complete most of her course work
9. they resented/be treated like third graders//be left out of the games

C. Complete the sentences. Use a perfect tense infinitive or gerund.

1. He is proud of **having discovered the South Pole**.
2. They hope _____.
3. The church expects _____.
4. She got tired from _____.

40 Summary of Verb + Infinitive and Verb + Gerund

She's **hoping to find** a spring dress.
He's **considered moving** to another city.
They'll **finish marking** the papers tomorrow.

A. Student 1: form a yes/no question. Use the present continuous tense. Student 2: answer with a negative or an affirmative sentence.

Ex. he wasn't/try/run away//get help
   Was he trying to run away?
   No, he was trying to get help.

1. they aren't/consider/move to the suburbs//buy a house in town
2. I'm not/admit/take the money//see it on the table
3. she isn't/hope/get a raise in pay//keep her job
4. we aren't/prepare/work in business//become teachers
5. he isn't/risk/lose his life//hurt his reputation
6. you weren't/agree/supply the cement//supply the sand

B. Student 1: ask a question word question. Student 2: answer with a full sentence. Use a–f.

1. What are you/consider/give to her	a. about 15
2. Who is/discuss/raise taxes	b. an Italian restaurant
3. When was he/hope/graduate	c. a jade bracelet
4. Where are you/plan/go to dinner	d. mine
5. How many kids are/try/get in the car	e. next year
6. Whose car is/begin/get old	f. the city government

1. **What are you considering giving to her?**
   I'm considering giving her a jade bracelet.

C. Form sentences with **but**. Use an affirmative clause, a negative clause, and the present perfect tense.

Ex. We/practice/throw the ball/catch the ball
   We've practiced throwing the ball, but we haven't practiced catching it.

1. The medicine/help/clear my nose/settle my stomach
2. They/finish/build the office building/build the parking garage
3. She/plan/go to Canada/drive there
4. I/agree/help with the park project/do the whole job
5. She/learn/play tennis/play very well
6. The city/delay/fix the streets/raise the property taxes

D. Read the statement. Then form another statement using the modal + verb in parentheses.

Ex. Mr. McGraw is always late for work. (should/ start)
   Mr. McGraw should start getting up earlier.

1. The Changs don't like their apartment. They want a house. (should/start)
2. Laura is leaving the office, and the safe is unlocked. She's thinking of something else. (might/forget)
3. My uncle smokes a lot and he feels bad. He's going to a doctor. (will/suggest)
4. My brother is practicing his violin in his room because my mother doesn't like the noise. (can't/stand)
5. It's a snowy day. The Rodriguezes are looking at travel brochures. (might/decide)

41 Verb + Infinitive: was going to

They **were going to** move, but now they're not.
I **wasn't going to** stay there all day.

A. Form a negative and an affirmative sentence. Use **wasn't/weren't going to** and **was/were going to**.

> **Ex.** I/take an umbrella//wear my raincoat
> **I wasn't going to take an umbrella. I was going to wear my raincoat.**

1. We/skip class//come in late
2. I/paint the furnace//clean it
3. They/burn the files//keep them in a safe
4. Some of the players/strike//play ball as usual
5. They/block off 18th Street//block off Lennox Avenue
6. The company/build a plant in Detroit//buy out a competitor there
7. The store/refund any money//give people replacements

B. Answer with **no** and a full sentence. Study the example.

> **Ex.** Are you going to spend your vacation at Turtle Lake?
> **No, I was going to spend it there, but I'm not now.**

1. Is the meeting going to be in room 602?
2. Are you going to get Sally a watch?
3. Is she going to translate all the letters?
4. Are the pilots going to go on strike?
5. Is the government going to reduce the income tax?
6. Are they going to use candles during the dinner?
7. Is the book going to have an appendix?
8. Are you going to keep paper on that shelf?
9. Is your uncle going to hunt deer this weekend?
10. Are they going to buy wooden skis?

C. Student 1: ask a question word question.
Student 2: answer with a full sentence. Both: use **was/were going to**.

1. what
   What was the child going to eat?
   She was going to eat a cookie.
2. where
3. how many
4. when

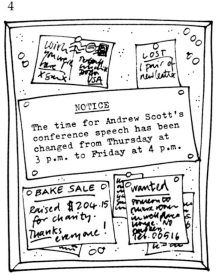

42 Verb + Infinitive: be to, be supposed to

You **are (not) to** use this door.
She **is (not) supposed to** begin yet.

A. These sentences are affirmative/negative pairs. Use **be (not) to** in 1–6 and **be (not) supposed to** in 7–12. Use the past tense where necessary.

1. Children **are to be** quiet at the table. They're **not to talk** all the time. (be, talk)
2. She _____ her dark glasses outside only. She _____ them on in the house. (wear, put)
3. Mr. Hingle _____ in court tomorrow. He _____ his court date. (appear, miss)
4. The label _____ all the ingredients, and they _____ in small print. (give, be)
5. He _____ on duty all day yesterday. He _____ the office. (be, leave)
6. You _____ the aluminum cans last week, but you _____ them in then. (collect, turn)
7. We're **supposed to sit** still. We _____ around. (sit, turn)
8. It _____ clear tomorrow. It _____. (be, rain)
9. The guards _____ around the building. They _____ at their posts. (walk, stay)
10. California _____ a wonderful place. It _____ bad weather. (be, have)
11. The Giants _____ yesterday's game. The Condors _____ them. (win, beat)
12. She _____ the report, but she forgot to. She _____ it by hand. (type, write)

B. Read the bus regulations. Then explain them to someone. Use **be (not) supposed to.**

Bus Regulations	
1. Pay exact fare when boarding.	4. No smoking on the bus.
2. Stand behind the white line.	5. Spitting is prohibited.
3. Do not talk to the operator.	6. Do not play radios.

1. **Passengers are supposed to pay the exact fare when boarding.**

C. Student 1: ask a question word question about the doctor's orders. Use **be supposed to.** Student 2: answer.

1. where
   Where's John supposed to stay?
   He's supposed to stay in bed.
2. what
3. how many
4. who

From the desk of
DR. JIM NELSON
_____

MUST Call:
John Martin - must continue
to stay in bed
Terry Featherston - no coffee
Bill Rodriguez - two heart
pills daily
Chris Walker - must stay
out of work for two weeks

43 Verb + Infinitive: used to as Past Habitual

What did she **use to** do?   She **used to** study.
Did she **use to** study?   She **didn't use to** work.

A. Read each sentence. Then form two sentences. Use **didn't use to**, **used to**, and the information in parentheses.

> **Ex.** Paul's a major. (a captain)
> **He didn't use to be one. He used to be a captain.**

1. They live in Texas. (in Illinois)
2. There's a bakery there. (a bookstore)
3. I eat soup for lunch. (a hamburger)
4. She shops at Treadwell's. (at Murphy's)
5. Our neighbor's son delivers the *Star*. (the *Times*)
6. He parks in the parking garage. (on the street)
7. They drive on the right side of the road in Sweden. (on the left)

B. Student 1: ask a yes/no question. Use **use to**.
Student 2: answer with **no, but** and a full sentence.

> **Ex.** know Mr. Wu//know his father
> **Did you use to know Mr. Wu?**
> **No, but I used to know his father.**

1. cook your own supper//cook my own breakfast
2. play the trumpet//play the violin
3. walk to work//walk home
4. wear a suit to work//wear a jacket
5. have a pet//take care of a neighbor's
6. work in a shoe factory//repair shoes
7. camp in the mountains//take hikes
8. go to the horse races//bet on the horses
9. work for a candidate//vote in every election

C. Student 1: read the sentence. Student 2: ask a question word question with **use to**. Student 1: answer with a complete sentence.

> **Ex.** Postage rates haven't always been this high. (how much//half)
> **How much did they use to be?**
> **They used to be only half as much.**

1. Tom hasn't always worked for Juan. (who//Fred)
2. My uncle hasn't always weighed so much. (how much//170 pounds)
3. Miss Fuller hasn't always driven to work. (how//take the bus)
4. I haven't always liked to watch baseball. (what//basketball)
5. The Ramons haven't always lived in Chicago. (where//Philadelphia)
6. Andy hasn't always dated Joyce. (who//Conchita)
7. The kids haven't always swum in this river. (where//in the lake)
8. That company hasn't always made toys. (what//machine equipment)
9. Senator Lenehan hasn't always voted so conservatively. (how//very liberally)
10. We haven't always gotten our hair cut at Dick's Barber Shop. (where//Ernie's Place)

44 Two-word Verbs: Separable Verbs

She **knocked** the water **over.**
She didn't **wipe** it **up.**

A. Read the sentence. Then form an affirmative or a negative sentence. Use an object pronoun with a verb from the list.

bring on	dream up	rub in
call off	write down	sort out
think over	fill up	take off
cut out		

Ex. I wore a jacket to the party.
I took it off there. (or) I didn't take it off.
1. She told me her phone number.
2. The company needs a new advertising plan.
3. She poured some oil on the wood.
4. His car ran out of gas.
5. She drew a pumpkin on some orange paper.
6. They're offering me a better job.
7. There were some ripe apples and some rotten ones in the box.
8. There was bad weather on the day of the picnic.
9. I always get colds in wet weather.

B. Student 1: read the sentence and ask a **what** question. Use **with.** Student 2: give an answer.

Ex. He wants to cut down the tree.
What can he cut it down with?
He can cut it down with an axe or a saw.

1. She wants to put on eye shadow.
2. He wants to scare away those dogs.
3. They want to put out the campfire.
4. I want to wash off this mud.
5. He wants to dig up the weeds.
6. She wants to pull out a gray hair.
7. The museum wants to close off one section.
8. They want to tear down that old building.

C. Student 1: ask a yes/no question. Student 2: answer with **no** and a full sentence. Use the two-word verb or noun object given.

Ex. A. did/he/his boots/take off//leave on
Did he take off his boots?
No, he left them on.

Ex. B. Liv/is/the radio/turning on//the stereo
Is Liv turning the radio on?
No, she's turning on the stereo.

1. have/left up/the posters/they//take down
2. did/pull out/the roots/you//leave in
3. the new restaurant/are/check out/going to/you//the new play
4. eat up/the children/the doughnuts/will//all the candy
5. fix up/that old house/they/will//tear down
6. he/in the safe/is/putting away/some money//take out
7. bring back/did/he/your lawn mower//my rake

4 5 Two-word and Three-word Verbs: Inseparable Verbs

Does the recipe **call for** raisins?
Yes, it **calls for** some.

A. Student 1: form a yes/no question. Student 2: answer with **no** and a full sentence.

Ex. by/did/go/he/the rules
Did he go by the rules?
No, he didn't go by the rules.

1. can/count/I/on/your attendance
2. fallen/for/has/she/your sweet words
3. anyone/at/did/laugh/your old jokes
4. children/do/easily/math/take/to
5. a smaller apartment/for/settle/will/you
6. antique furniture/deal/does/that company/in
7. are/going to/into/look/the cause of the accident/you
8. across/any interesting clues/come/have/the police/yet
9. always/does/him/his little sister/on/tell

B. Fill in the blanks with the correct three-word verb.

catch up to	go back on
catch up with	look out for
come down with	miss out on
get away with	

1. We didn't see you at the party. You certainly **missed out on** a good time last night.
2. You'd better wear a jacket. You don't want to _____ a cold.
3. The Giants aren't playing well tonight. They need ten points to _____ the Kings.
4. Deer cross the highway here. Motorists often have to _____ them.
5. The company shouldn't cut everyone's pay. They'll never _____ it.
6. But, Henry, you promised you'd help me organize the party. You can't _____ your word.
7. Mohammed left about ten minutes ago. If you hurry, you can _____ him.
8. When you're driving, you have to _____ other drivers. They don't always obey all the traffic laws.

C. Answer the questions with full sentences. Use a pronoun and a separable or an inseparable two-word or three-word verb from the list.

calm down	look into
come down with	sleep on
take to	stick to
fall for	tell on

Ex. Do you enjoy your new hobby?
I've really taken to it.

1. What are the police doing about the theft?
2. What's he done about the frightened children?
3. What did Sally do after the boys bothered her?
4. Is she going to do anything about the problem now?
5. Will he quit the project?
6. The professor has fainted. Could he be ill?
7. Is Mike in love with your roommate?

46 Verb Complements: Question Word Clause

I know
I'll explain to you } **what** she wants.

A. Student 1: ask a question by matching **do you know** with a question word (1–10) and a phrase (a–j).
Student 2: give the best answer you can.

1. what
2. where
3. how
4. who
5. when

6. why
7. how much
8. how many
9. how long
10. how big

a. the post office is
b. passengers a 747 airplane holds
c. the date is
d. a color TV costs
e. discovered the South Pole

f. a camera works
g. vaccines work
h. the Moon is
i. the Nile River is
j. Halley's comet will return

1. **Do you know what the date is?**
   It's (today's date).

B. Answer the questions with a full sentence. Use a
question word clause as object.

1. What's she deciding?
   She's deciding which college is best. (or) . . .
   where she wants to study.
2. What's she thinking about?
3. What did she see?
4. What's he showing her?

C. Read the first sentence. Then fill in the blanks to
complete the second one with a question word
clause.

1. I don't see my other shoe. I wonder **where I
   put it**. (or) . . . **what happened to it**.
2. Pete wore a costume. No one guessed
   _____.
3. Ms. Wang went to hotel management school.
   She learned _____.
4. There was a lot of noise on the radio. I couldn't
   hear _____.

5. My sister hid her ring in her bedroom. Now she
   can't remember _____.
6. Uncle Tony keeps an old baseball bat in his room.
   It reminds him of _____.
7. I can't find Bhutan on the map. Please show me
   _____.
8. The storm will strike soon. We're trying to figure
   out _____.
9. This button turns the computer on and off, but I
   can't understand _____.
10. His brother wants a sweater, but he's not sure
    _____.

47 Verb Complements: if or whether Clause

I don't know
{
if I'll go (or not).
whether (or not) I'll go (or not).
}

A. Complete the answer. Use a **whether** clause.

1. Did Amy pay the tax? I don't know **whether she paid it (or not)**.
2. Will you buy a trailer? I'm still deciding _____.
3. Has Alberto paid his tuition? They're checking to see _____.
4. Do they offer discounts? We haven't found out _____.

5. Did Mary Anne get a promotion? I didn't hear _____.
6. Did the speaker go to Harvard? I didn't find out _____.
7. Is the professor going to give a test? No one's sure _____.
8. Did you turn off the stove? I can't remember _____.

B. Student 1: ask **What's he/she wondering?**
Student 2: answer with a full sentence. Use an **if** clause.

1. What's he wondering?
   He's wondering if the oasis is real. (or) . . . **if he'll find water soon.** (or) . . . **if the oasis is a mirage.**

C. Read the first sentence. Then complete the second one with a **whether or not** clause.

1. The caller didn't speak clearly. I couldn't tell **whether or not it was a man.** (or) . . . **whether or not he was an American.**
2. The thief left quickly. I didn't notice _____.
3. Our neighbors' house is for sale. We're considering _____.
4. Osmin's doctor wants to operate on him. He hasn't made a decision _____.
5. They're investigating Linda's income. They want to know _____.

6. Arlene doesn't like her job. She's uncertain _____.
7. He wants tickets for the play. He's not sure _____.
8. A news reporter interviewed Mayor Gardner. She wanted to find out _____.
9. They're speaking some European language. I can't tell _____.
10. Lois was going to come to this concert. I can't see _____.

48 Verb Complements: Question Word + Infinitive

I wonder **whether** (or not) to go (or not).
I'll show you **what** to do next.

A. Student 1: ask a yes/no question by matching clauses from 1–8 and a–h. Student 2: respond with some kind of logical answer. (Note: many more than eight questions can be made; there is no one correct answer.)

1. Do you know
2. Have you ever wondered
3. Have you decided
4. Do you remember
5. Did you understand
6. Can you find out
7. Does anyone know
8. Have you ever forgotten

a. where to go in case of fire
b. what to do in an emergency
c. how to spell a word
d. where to apply for a visa
e. how to operate a computer
f. how to bring about world peace
g. how to drive a car
h. what to do on your next vacation

1. **Do you know where to apply for a visa?**
   Yes, you go to the embassy or consulate of the country you intend to visit.

B. Read the first sentence. Then complete the second one with a question word and an infinitive. (Do not use **whether** in this exercise.)

1. Your bicycle is broken. I'll show you **how to fix it**. (or) . . . **where to take it**.
2. We can get a refund. Let's find out _____.
3. The astronauts are off course. They don't know _____.
4. Thanks for explaining. Now I understand _____.
5. Nadia has been accepted at three colleges. She's not sure _____.
6. The Carlbergs want to invite some people. They can't decide _____.
7. Tomorrow is her boyfriend's birthday. She's wondering _____.
8. We need to get on Route 357. You should find out _____.
9. Please deal the cards more carefully. You should know _____.
10. There will be a fire drill sometime. No one knows _____.

C. Answer with a full sentence. Use **whether or not** and an infinitive.

Ex. Do we add sugar to the recipe? (find out)
   I'll find out whether or not to add it.

1. Are we supposed to turn the switch off now? (am not sure)
2. Are they going to trade in their old car? (don't know)
3. Do you think we should keep the bad news from Janet's mother? (don't know)
4. Is Conley going to the conference in Chicago? (is in doubt)
5. Does Donna need a new vacuum cleaner? (is doubtful)
6. Are the secretaries going to eat lunch at Tiny's? (are not sure)
7. Does the typewriter need a new ribbon? (don't know)

 49 Cause or Reason: because

because of her injury
because she injured herself

A. Form two sentences. Use **because** and **because of**.

Ex. They postponed the party/it was snowing hard//the heavy snow
They postponed the party because it was snowing hard.
They postponed the party because of the heavy snow.

1. I'm going to the doctor/I don't feel well//my upset stomach
2. Food prices are high now/the dry weather//the weather's been very dry
3. The kids are playing indoors/it's raining outside// the rain
4. Betty left the theater/she didn't like the film//the bad acting in the film
5. The company moved to Plainfield/taxes are lower there/the lower taxes there
6. The bus is stuck/a flat tire//one of its tires is flat
7. He couldn't eat the beans/all the salt//they were too salty
8. I can't study/it's too noisy//the noise
9. Mamoru was late/the heavy traffic//the traffic was heavy

B. Combine the sentences. Make one into a **because** clause.

Ex. The soldiers were nervous. The soldiers were smoking.
The soldiers were smoking because they were nervous.

1. I didn't have lunch. I'm hungry.
2. The weather changed. A cold front moved in.
3. She's smiling. He remembered their wedding anniversary.
4. They serve good seafood there. I eat there.
5. The sunlight isn't good today. She can't paint today.
6. Our costs went up. We're raising our prices.
7. His car wasn't running well. He took his car to the garage.
8. There are holes in the road. They're working on the road.
9. This scale isn't accurate. We need a new scale.
10. He seemed very friendly. She asked him out.

C. Answer with a full sentence. Use **because** or **because of**.

Ex. Why was Mrs. Takano absent?
She was absent because she was sick. (or) . . .
because she had a bad cold.

1. Why couldn't you take a bus?
2. Why didn't she eat the candy with the nuts and chocolate?
3. Why did Mr. Salvatore cry?
4. Why's the TV off?
5. Why can't he give you a ride?
6. Why don't they play tennis outdoors in the winter?
7. Why did he lose the election?
8. Why's that window broken?

50 Cause or Reason: since, now that

since you're a senator (now)
now that you're a senator

A. Combine the sentences. Use **since** with the cause or reason clause.

> **Ex.** I wore my brown suit. My blue suit was at the cleaners.
> **Since my blue suit was at the cleaners, I wore my brown one.**

1. The history teacher was absent. They showed us a film.
2. The dog wasn't very active. The dog was old.
3. There was no rain. We had to irrigate the fields.
4. I've already read the paper. The paper comes in the morning.
5. He can leave school any time. He finished all his exams.
6. She broke her leg. She had to go to the hospital.
7. There's no electricity. We can't stay up very late.

B. Form sentences with a **now that** or a **since** clause.

> **Ex.** Bill has a kite/he/fly it
> **Now that Bill has a kite, he's going to fly it.**

1. Mr. Fry has left the room/the students/play
2. the car is running well again/I/drive to work
3. the weather's getting hotter/we/go to the beach
4. Laura and Lars are friends/they/come to parties together
5. his phone has been busy for two hours/I/leave him a note
6. Ms. McGarvey's working downtown/she/take the subway
7. Watkins has published his first book/he/write another one
8. we'll be picking her up in the car/she/have more time to get ready
9. I've spent all my money/I/stay home
10. the boy is sick/he/stay in bed
11. it's time to go/we/get our coats

C. Complete the cause or reason clause in these sentences.

1. Since **they had a fire last night**, the store is closed today.
2. Since _____, I can't buy my shoes.
3. Since _____, let's go on a picnic.
4. Since _____, I'll get you some postage stamps.
5. Since _____, I'm going to bet on the Robins.
6. Since _____, I'm going to send her a gift.
7. Since _____, Louise will have to take more math courses.
8. Since _____, Ms. Grayson will be out of the office all day.

51 Purpose: Infinitive

He's studying (**in order**) **to become a dentist.**
He paid a dollar **for me to watch his car**.

A. Form two sentences with infinitives of purpose. Study the example.

    Ex. He's going to the garden/get some carrots//eat for supper
    He's going to the garden to get some carrots.
    He's getting some carrots to eat for supper.

  1. She's taking a shower/get cleaned up//go to a dance
  2. I went to the library/borrow a book//learn about losing weight
  3. Mr. Blake bought a ticket/fly to Newfield//sign a contract
  4. Paul will go to the department store/buy a suit//wear to the wedding
  5. He went to the bank/take out some money//buy a new motorcycle
  6. She got out a shovel/dig a hole//plant the rosebush
  7. He's working overtime/make some extra money//buy a new car
  8. She's selling her car/get $2,000//pay her bills
  9. I want to borrow the car/go to the swimming pool//cool off
  10. You can go to an ear doctor/get a hearing aid//improve your hearing
  11. She went to the kitchen/make some coffee//warm herself up

---

B. Student 1: ask a **why** question about each picture.
Student 2: answer with an infinitive of purpose.

  1. Why was that boy saving money?
  (In order) To buy a car.

C. Match sentences 1–6 with a–f. Make a–f into infinitive phrases with **for**.

  1. I brought an extra umbrella.
  2. We made a trap.
  3. Mrs. Hall left a message.
  4. That company publishes books.
  5. I have a question.
  6. I'll peel an orange.

  a. Foreign students can use them to learn English.
  b. Ms. Fuller will ask the computer.
  c. Pat can use it.
  d. Harry will catch mice.
  e. The secretary will give it to Marisa.
  f. You can eat it.

  1. I brought an extra umbrella for Pat to use.

52 Purpose: so that

I'll close the window **so (that) the room will stay warm.**
I closed the window **so (that) the room would stay warm.**

A. Combine the sentences. Use **so that** with the purpose clause.

Ex. He'll use red ink. The numbers will stand out.
He'll use red ink so (that) the numbers will stand out.

1. They bought a second car. They each could use a car.
2. A lot of people will hear about it. They're advertising on the radio.
3. Shirley could grow big tomatoes. Shirley used a lot of fertilizer.
4. Miss Lane put on a shower cap. Miss Lane could keep her hair dry.
5. I could save some money. I took a bus.
6. Students can check their answers. There's an answer key in the book.
7. He can tell his wife the good news himself. He's hurrying home.

B. Match questions 1–8 with sentences a–h. Use a–h in a **so that** clause.

1. Why is Ali taking the subway?
2. Why are you giving me a quarter?
3. Why did Mr. Garth move over?
4. Why is she putting her coat on the seat?
5. Why did she start the car?
6. Why are they closing the store?
7. Why did they mark the package?
8. Why are you buying such expensive chairs?

a. The mechanic could listen to the engine.
b. They won't wear out in a few years.
c. He'll get to work on time.
d. The post office would be careful with it.
e. They can take inventory.
f. Other people can't sit there.
g. You can make a phone call.
h. You could put your package on this seat.

1. **So that he'll get to work on time.**

C. Student 1: ask a **why** question about the items on Sandy's shopping list. Student 2: answer like the example. Use a **so** clause.

Ex. Why is Sandy going to buy some apples?
I don't know—maybe so she can make an apple pie.

Shopping List
_____

dozen apples
soup bone
picnic basket
envelopes
videotape
bird seed
hammer and nails
one gallon blue paint
fertilizer
bicycle

53 Condition: Affirmative if Clauses

I'll **have** coffee **if you make some**.
If you make coffee, I'll **have** some.

A. Match sentences 1–8 and a–h. Make a–h into an **if** clause.

1. I'll be very glad.
2. I'll buy those things.
3. I'll give a big party.
4. I'll start again.
5. We'll believe you.
6. We'll go hiking.
7. We'll go to the beach.
8. We'll send the food back to the kitchen.

a. I get a raise.
b. I make a mistake.
c. It's hot.
d. It's cold.
e. The weather improves.
f. They go on sale.
g. We win this game.
h. You show us a picture of it.

1. **I'll be very glad if I get a raise.**

B. Student 1: read the sentence. Ask **what will you do if . . . .** Student 2: give a logical answer. Use a full sentence with an **if** clause.

Ex. Maybe the door will be locked.
What will you do if the door's locked?
If it's locked, I'll climb in a window.

1. Maybe they won't have lasagna.
2. Maybe it'll be raining hard.
3. Maybe the sweater will be the wrong size.
4. Maybe they'll raise your rent.
5. Maybe the lights will go out.

C. Combine the sentences. Make one into an **if** clause. Use the clauses in the given order.

Ex. A. You'll send the check today. They'll get the check on the fourth.
If you send the check today, they'll get it on the fourth.

Ex. B. I'll go to the doctor. My back will begin to ache again.
I'll go to the doctor if my back begins to ache again.

1. You'll turn this handle. An alarm will sound.
2. The police will give you a reward. You'll give the police information.
3. José can run in the race. José will bring a letter from his doctor.
4. You can make $100 extra. You will work overtime this weekend.
5. I could translate this letter for you. I had my dictionary here.
6. We can save enough money. We may go to Japan this summer.
7. Take lessons from Mr. Bell. You want to play the trumpet.
8. You feel dizzy. Take this medicine.
9. Eat good food and exercise every day. You want to be healthy.
10. You need an application form. Write to our home office.

54 Condition: unless and Negative if

I won't go **unless she goes**.
I won't go **if she doesn't** (go).

A. Combine the sentences. Make a–h into an **unless** clause.

1. I won't eat hamburgers.	**a.** She wants to walk.
2. Our dog doesn't bark.	**b.** A stranger comes into the yard.
3. You can't take the typewriter home.	**c.** It's raining hard.
4. You won't lose much weight.	**d.** You want to do something else.
5. We'll play tennis Saturday.	**e.** You leave a deposit.
6. He'll give Rosina a ride.	**f.** They have ketchup on them.
7. You can't rent a car.	**g.** You have a driver's license.
8. Tom always walks to work.	**h.** You exercise harder.

1. I won't eat hamburgers unless they have ketchup on them.

B. Combine the sentences. Make one into an **if** or **unless** clause. Use the clauses in the given order.

Ex. I'll take you home now. You aren't enjoying the program.
I'll take you home now if you aren't enjoying the program.

1. I'll be in the office tomorrow. I don't have to be in St. Louis.
2. She can't go to the dance. She promises to be home by midnight.
3. They will lower the price. I won't buy the car.
4. I go to the dentist. I don't have toothaches.
5. He can borrow her car. She doesn't have to use her car.
6. You can guess at the answers on the test. You aren't sure of the answers.
7. She's not going out today. There isn't any food for supper.
8. I'll help you look for your wallet. You can't find your wallet.

C. Student 1: ask a question (a–e) about one of the pictures.
Student 2: answer with **no** and a full sentence. Use an **unless** or a negative **if** clause.

a. Can't you open this?
b. Can't I use this one?
c. Can't I get in?
d. Won't I pass?
e. Won't they admit her?

1. Can't I get in?
No, you can't get in unless you're 17 years old.

55 Condition: Unreal if

I would (I'd) go **if she were going**.
I wouldn't go **if she didn't go**.

A. Read the questions and give a short **no** answer. Then use **but** and a full sentence.

  Ex. Will you buy a fur coat?
  No, I won't. But I'd buy one if I could.

  1. Will she deduct those expenses from her tax?

  2. Will they promote Mohammed to chief of production?
  3. Will the company borrow $40,000?
  4. Will she bring Jason with her?
  5. Will you take a long vacation this year?

B. Student 1: read the sentence. Student 2: ask a yes/no question. Use **would . . . if . . . .** Student 1: give a short answer.

  Ex. I won't go because you're not going.
  Would you go if I were going?
  Yes, I would.

  1. He won't play baseball because Art and Luis aren't playing.
  2. They won't refund the money because he doesn't have the sales slip.
  3. I can't drink the tea because it doesn't have sugar in it.
  4. My roommate can't go swimming because she doesn't have a suit.

  5. I won't go to Dr. Warner because I don't like her.
  6. Erik can't get that job because he didn't finish college.
  7. They can't deliver the rug today because the drivers are on strike.
  8. She doesn't have time to meet them at the airport because she has so much work to do at the office.
  9. I won't have dessert because I'm watching my weight.
  10. They'll stay home because the baby is sick.
  11. I don't have extra money to spend because I need it for a doctor's bill.
  12. I can park here because I have a special sticker on my car.
  13. We'll use my office because they're painting the conference room.

C. Student 1: ask a question word question. Use **you** with an **if** clause. Student 2: give a logical answer.

  Ex. had a toothache
  What would you do if you had a toothache?
  I'd see the dentist.
  (or) **Where would you go if you had a toothache?**
  I'd go to the dentist.

  1. had too much to carry
  2. saw a snake
  3. found a lot of money
  4. saw an accident
  5. needed shoes
  6. did not feel well
  7. were late for work
  8. had some free time

56 Condition: Past Unreal if

I would have gone **if she had gone**.
I wouldn't have gone **if she hadn't gone**.

A. Student 1: ask a yes/no question. Student 2: give a short **no** answer. Then use **but** to start a full sentence with an **if** clause.

Ex. They didn't win the volleyball game because Liz didn't play.
Did they win the volleyball game?
No, they didn't. But they would have won it if Liz had played.

1. He didn't get the sunglasses because he found his other pair.
2. They couldn't drive up the mountain because their car wasn't running well.
3. Carmen couldn't write the report because her assistant hadn't tallied the figures.
4. They didn't answer the ad because they didn't have enough money.
5. Mr. Burton didn't answer you because he didn't hear you.
6. Ms. Elkins wasn't at the meeting because she wasn't feeling well.
7. I didn't mail the letter because I didn't have any stamps.
8. We weren't worried because we didn't know his background.
9. He couldn't open the lock because he couldn't remember the combination.

B. Student 1: read the sentence. Student 2: respond **Oh, I wouldn't have done that.** Add a full sentence with an **if** clause.

Ex. I saw a bear and climbed a tree.
Oh, I wouldn't have done that. If I had seen a bear, I would have stood perfectly still.

1. He ran out of gas and called a garage.
2. Teresa was late for work and went through a yellow light.
3. Patterson was angry at his friend and threw a book at him.
4. He tore his shirt and bought a new one.
5. I saw the accident and panicked.
6. Judy went to Japan and stayed in Tokyo all the time.
7. Harvey got some extra money and played video games.

C. Student 1: read the question. Student 2: answer with a **because** clause. Student 1: then ask a yes/no question. Student 2: give a short **yes** answer.

1. Why didn't she go hiking?
Because she was sick in bed.
Would she have gone hiking if she hadn't been sick?
Yes, she would have.
2. Why didn't he drive to the party?
3. Why couldn't anyone call her?
4. Why weren't the guests satisfied?

57 Concession: although, in spite of

Although she's old, she's very active.
In spite of her age, she's very active.

A. Form sentences. Use **although** or **in spite of** to connect phrases 1–8 with a–h.

1. Ari runs well
2. I read a lot
3. The water's cold
4. Carolyn used that towel
5. The Polar Bear Club goes swimming in the winter
6. We bought the $400 encyclopedia
7. He wore the suit
8. The car's engine froze

a. his sore leg
b. it seemed expensive
c. it was already wet
d. it was out of style
e. my poor eyesight
f. the air's quite hot
g. the antifreeze
h. the cold

1. Ari runs well in spite of his sore leg.

B. Complete the sentences. Use an **although** clause.

1. She's going swimming **although the weather isn't good**. (or) . . . **although it's chilly**.
2. She got to the meeting on time _____.
3. He hurt his head _____.
4. Someone was skating _____.

C. Student 1: ask a yes/no question. Student 2: give a short **yes** or **no** answer with an **even though** clause.

Ex. You caught the bus. (You left the house late.)
Did you catch the bus?
Yes, I did—even though I left the house late.

1. Your friend looks nice. (She is wearing old clothes.)
2. The horses didn't go near the hay. (They were hungry.)
3. I couldn't find the planet Saturn. (I had my telescope.)
4. I recognized Mr. Stone. (He tried to hide behind a curtain.)
5. The kite flew. (It didn't have a tail.)
6. My sister eats peanut butter. (She doesn't like peanuts.)
7. He got another haircut. (His hair wasn't very long.)
8. This milk is all right. (Someone left it out of the refrigerator.)
9. She drove her car to work this morning. (She couldn't find her glasses.)

58 Concession: but Conjunction

She is old,
She may be old, } **but** she's very active (anyway).

A. Student 1: read the question. Student 2: answer with a full sentence. Begin **Yes, it may take me/him/her/them all day, but . . . .**

Ex. Are you going to weed the whole garden?
Yes, it may take me all day, but I'm going to weed it.

1. Is Mr. Somers going to find the leak in the roof?
2. Are you going to read that novel?
3. Will Dolores finish the *Times* crossword puzzle?
4. Is Emma going to write all ten letters?
5. Will the Arlottos rebuild their fence?
6. Will the music teacher teach that song to the first grade?
7. Is the doctor going to see all those people?
8. Does she iron the clothes for the whole family?
9. Will you type all those pages?

B. Combine the sentences. Use **may** or **might** in the first clause and connect with **but** in the other.

Ex. Bob went to the picnic. Bob didn't feel well.
Bob may (or might) not have felt well, but he went on the picnic anyway.

1. You have to type these pages. You have a sore finger.
2. Ms. Sickenberger has an odd name. Ms. Sickenberger is very popular.
3. The house is old. The house is in excellent condition.
4. The play was very effective. The play wasn't particularly well written.
5. I don't believe it. They say they saw a UFO.
6. You were late to work. You left home on time this morning.
7. She watched the whole movie. The movie wasn't very good.
8. The music wasn't played well. We enjoyed the child's performance.
9. There's someone inside. The house may look empty.

C. Complete the sentences with a **but** clause.

1. Gail may be older than Beverly, **but she's not as tall.** (or) . . . **but Beverly's taller.**
2. Boston may be an old city, _____.
3. Mrs. Burch may like cake, _____.
4. Contestant 17 may have sung well, _____.

59 Degree: so or such + that Clause of Result

The handle is **so hot**
That's **such a hot handle** } **(that)** I can't touch it.

A. Fill in the blanks with **so** or **such** and complete sentences 1–10 with a **that** clause from sentences a–j.

1. This is _____ good soup
2. I had _____ a big bowl of soup
3. He was _____ curious about magic
4. She had _____ a soft mattress
5. Her ankle hurt _____ badly
6. He became _____ clever a salesman
7. She vacuums the rug _____ often
8. The Cookie Place is doing _____ a good business
9. There was _____ a long line at the post office
10. _____ loud voices were coming from the room

a. He always tried to learn new tricks.
b. I couldn't eat it all.
c. I'm going to have more.
d. It hurt her back.
e. It took me half an hour to get some stamps.
f. She could hardly walk.
g. She's wearing it out.
h. They're going to move to a larger location.
i. We were afraid to knock on the door.
j. Few customers could refuse him.

1. **This is such good soup (that) I'm going to have more.**

B. Answer with **yes** or **no** and a sentence. Use **so** or **such** and a **that** clause with the word in parentheses.

Ex. Did many dishes break? (many)
Yes, so many dishes broke that we had to use paper plates. (or) . . . we fired the dishwasher.

1. Did many members attend? (few)
2. Did much sugar spill? (much)
3. Was much of the fish unsafe? (little)
4. Did many people answer the ad? (a lot of)
5. Did the report take much time? (little)
6. Did many plants survive the winter? (few)
7. Did much dirt get in the bathtub? (a lot of)
8. Does he play video games much? (little)

C. Student 1: ask a **how** question using the word given. Student 2: answer with a full sentence like the example.

1. old
   How old is the car?
   It's such an old one that it's an antique.
2. strong
3. hard
4. perfect

60 Degree: too or enough + Infinitive of Result

The handle is **too hot**
That's **too hot a handle** } (for me) to touch.

A. Answer with **yes** or **no** and a full sentence. Use **too** or **enough** and the word(s) in parentheses.

Ex. Can you lift that box? (light)
Yes, it's light enough to lift.

1. Can you move those logs? (heavy)
2. Can you still see the airplane? (far away)
3. Can you do the third problem? (easy)
4. Are you able to understand the instructions? (simple)
5. Could you pick them up at the airport? (sick)
6. Were you able to finish the laundry? (much)
7. Were you able to fix the radio? (easy)

B. Student 1: ask yes/no questions about Ruth Brown, 70 years old, and her five-year-old grandson, Bobby. Use **too** or **enough** and the adjectives **young** or **old**. Student 2: answer with **yes** or **no** and a full sentence.

Ex. go to school
Is Bobby old enough to go to school?
Yes, he's old enough for that.

1. get a job
2. be retired
3. drive a car
4. ride a bicycle
5. get married
6. ride the bus free
7. take out a life insurance policy

C. Form sentences. Use **too** or **enough** in a noun phrase containing the adjectives given.

1. cold
   It's not a cold enough day for them to skate.
2. expensive
3. big
4. young

61 Subjunctive: Verbs of Persuasion

They $\left\{\begin{array}{l} \text{insist} \\ \text{insisted} \end{array}\right\}$ (that) she (not) **try** it again.

A. Student 1: ask a yes/no question. Use a **that** clause with the base verb form. Student 2: answer with **no** and a full sentence. Omit **that**.

> **Ex.** you suggest/she/take Route 79//continue on Route 401
> **Do you suggest that she take Route 79?**
> **No, I suggest she continue on Route 401.**

1. you insist/he/eat everything on his plate//eat some of each food
2. the Torreses prefer/we/visit them next week// visit them now
3. the president is asking/Congress/revise the election law//change the tax law
4. the police officer ordered/the man/put his hands up//put them behind his back
5. they advised/Michaela/go into accounting//take up a musical instrument
6. the school is urging/parents/stay at home//visit their child's school
7. the union has demanded/the company/not hire new workers//not fire any present workers
8. his father has insisted/he/paint the house//paint the steps
9. the waiter suggests/they/order steak//order the fish

B. Student 1: read the sentence. Student 2: ask a yes/no question. Begin **is it . . .** or **was it . . . .** Student 1: answer with **Yes, it certainly is/was.**

> **Ex.** He'll fill out another form. (necessary)
> **Is it necessary that he do that?**
> **Yes, it certainly is.**

1. We'll install a fire alarm. (advisable)
2. She'll move to a lower floor. (suggested)
3. They will follow later in another car. (better)
4. Mr. Arnold signed the card twice. (required)
5. We registered the letter. (advisable)
6. Harry saw a doctor right away. (urgent)
7. They planted the bushes in the shade. (important)

C. Student 1: ask a **what** question. Student 2: answer with a full sentence.

> **Ex. What's the doctor advising him to do?**
> **He's advising that he not eat fatty foods.**

From the desk of
DR. JIM NELSON

List of things to tell Arnold
Rodriguez:
Don't eat fatty foods
Cut down on alcohol and sugar
Don't drink any coffee or tea
Begin an exercise program
Get eight hours of sleep
Lose at least 25 pounds

62 Subjunctive: Verbs wish vs. hope

I **wish** (that) she were here now.
I **hope** (that) she is here now.

I **wish** (that) he'd go away.
I **hope** (that) he goes away soon.

A. Fill in the blanks with the correct form of a verb from the list. Use the verb **be** more than once. In sentences 6–10 use **would** or **had** plus a verb.

be	begin	handle	give
tell	not charge	have	find

1. I wish I ___were___ at the beach now.
2. Gene wishes he _____ a new bathing suit.
3. They wish they _____ some large advertising accounts.
4. I wish there _____ weather reports every hour on TV.
5. She wishes the museum _____ admission.
6. Helen Anthony wishes she _____ her doctor.
7. I wish the dog _____ quiet next door. I can't sleep.
8. They wish they _____ the project two weeks ago.
9. He wishes they _____ a prize for good intentions.
10. She wishes her husband _____ a job as good as hers.

B. Form two sentences. Begin with **I wish . . .** and **I hope . . . .**

Ex. They don't sell sports equipment. Maybe they sell pet supplies.
I wish they sold sports equipment. I hope they sell pet supplies anyway.

1. She doesn't have a compact disc player. Maybe she'll get one for her birthday.
2. Andrea doesn't play the guitar. Maybe she plays the piano.
3. The roads aren't plowed. Maybe the snow isn't too deep.
4. There isn't a mail delivery today. Maybe my letter will come tomorrow.
5. The baby is crying. Maybe he'll stop soon.
6. The files are wet. Maybe they're still readable.
7. Tom Shipley is on vacation this week. Maybe he'll return early.
8. The clerk has a cold. Maybe it isn't a serious one.
9. This job takes an hour. Maybe I can leave by noon.

C. Imagine you are the person in the picture. Form two sentences using **wish** and **hope**.

1. **I wish he'd play more softly. I hope he stops soon.**

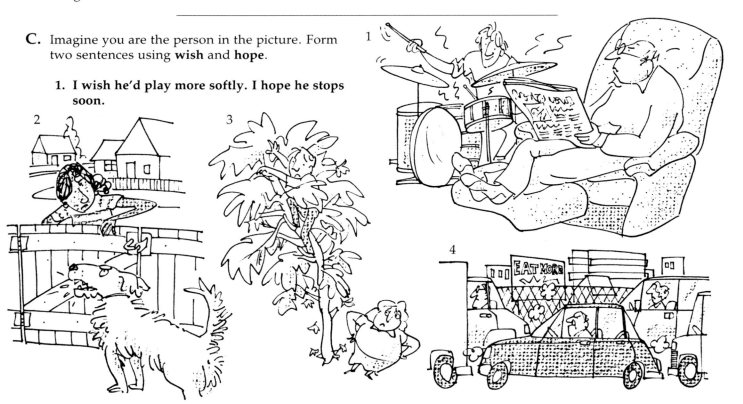

63 Indirect Speech: Statements

"I am ready."   **He said** (that) he was/is ready.
"I was ready."   **He said** (that) he was ready.

A. Student 1: read the direct quote. Student 2: ask
"What did you say?" Student 1: give an indirect
statement. Use **I said.**

Ex. "I'm upset about that news."
What did you say?
I said I was upset about that news.

1. "Bill and Terry are out of town."
2. "They're taking a computer course."
3. "He isn't learning much about life."
4. "I always take the Fifth Avenue bus."
5. "It rains almost every afternoon."
6. "Mercedes blew up 17 balloons."
7. "They've turned their TV set off."
8. "It's going to be cold tomorrow."
9. "Doctors really are busy people."
10. "There are just a few wild animals around here."
11. "We don't sell typing paper here."
12. "The experts are not always right."
13. "She doesn't pay her electric bill until the last minute."
14. "There's never been an invention like sliced bread."

B. Report David and Janet Smith's dialogue. Use indirect quotes with **that.**

1. David told Janet that he was in a hurry.

64 Indirect Speech: Statements with Modals

"He won't help."   **She said** (that) he **wouldn't** help.
"He wouldn't help."   **She said** (that) he **wouldn't** help.

A. Student 1: read the quote. Student 2: ask a yes/no question about the quote. Use **did you say . . . .** Student 1: answer with **Yes, that's right.**

Ex. "I can pick you up."
Did you say you could pick me up?
Yes, that's right.

1. "I'll be ready at five."
2. "The other people won't mind."
3. "You can't change your mind now."
4. "She must be quite successful."
5. "We must order more paper towels."
6. "You may hang your coat here."
7. "He must not spend all his time with Tina."
8. "We couldn't use Summit Avenue."
9. "No one should go outside in this weather without a hat."
10. "It might take more than two hours."
11. "Harold should remember his appointments."
12. "You might not get another chance."
13. "The store will be decorating for Mother's Day next week."
14. "We should be getting an answer from the foundation soon."
15. "They must be spending a fortune on doctor bills."
16. "You should be warming up in the other room."
17. "Some of the players might not be returning next year."
18. "He shouldn't have paid the plumber yet."
19. "I must have missed something."
20. "Ms. Tendall wouldn't have done a thing like that."
21. "The schedule won't have changed."
22. "Your quarter may have fallen into a hole."
23. "The lock can be changed for you."
24. "No one will be left out."

B. Student 1: ask a question using the question word given. Include a clause of indirect speech. Student 2: answer with a full sentence using indirect speech.

1. how much
   How much did the mechanic say the job would cost?
   He said it would cost $465.88.
2. when
3. which
4. what

65 Indirect Speech: Questions

"Are you ready?"   **He asked** if I was ready (or not).
"Where are you?"   **He asked** where I was.

A. Student 1: read the direct quote. Student 2: ask
What did you say? Student 1: give an indirect
quote. Use **asked if**.

    Ex. "Are any tomatoes ripe yet?"
    What did you say?
    I asked if any tomatoes were ripe yet.

1. "Are there any radios cheaper than this?"
2. "Do you have any cheaper radios?"
3. "Do you want to know her address?"
4. "Are you looking for her address?"
5. "Does the business outlook look better?"
6. "Is business going to improve?"
7. "Did that tomato look ripe to you?"
8. "Is it time for bed already?"
9. "Will we have to go to bed soon?"
10. "Were you satisfied with the color of the curtains?"
11. "Did the color of the rug satisfy you?"
12. "Has the dog been fed?"
13. "Is the dog eating its food?"
14. "Can John and Akiko see the pictures?"
15. "Are Mr. and Mrs. Rodríguez looking at them?"
16. "Is there a pencil in that drawer?"
17. "Do you see my red pencil over there?"
18. "Are there two b's in the name Webber?"
19. "Is the name Webber spelled with two b's?"
20. "Has there been any rain this week?"

B. First read these dialogues.

Stranger:	Where's the post office?
Police officer:	It's that tall white building on the next block.
Salesperson:	Is this the TV you're asking about? This color model right here, with remote control, is $499.
Mrs. Todd:	Oh, my. That's more than I intended to pay.
Paul:	When are our book reports due, Mrs. Whitaker?
Teacher:	All reports are due next Monday, without exception.
Pedestrian 1:	Yes, I have the time. It's exactly 3:15.
Pedestrian 2:	Thank you very much.
Alice:	What kind of work do you do, Walter?
Walter:	I'm a newspaper photographer.
Ted:	How did you like the movie?
Jean:	I thought it was super!
Mr. Jordan:	What does "frenetic" mean, Jean?
Mrs. Jordan:	It means "frantic" or "frenzied."

Now answer the questions with a full sentence.
Use a question word clause as object.

    Ex. What did the stranger want to know?
    He/She wanted to know where the post office was.

1. What did Mrs. Todd ask the salesperson?
2. What wasn't Paul sure about?
3. What did one pedestrian ask another?
4. What was Alice wondering about?
5. What did Ted inquire about?
6. What did Mr. Jordan want to know?

C. Student 1: ask questions using question words from the list. Student 2: say **I'm sorry, I didn't hear you.**
Student 1: give an indirect quote. Student 2: answer.

    who   what kind   whose   what   which   where   when   how many   how   why

Ex. Who's driving car number 16?
I'm sorry, I didn't hear you.
I asked who was driving car
number 16.
Oh, Dick Clift is.

Place	Car	Driver	Auto	Time	Lap No.	Comments
1	41	Doyle Bowers	Porsche	1:15:51	225	in pit stop
2	16	Dick Clift	Ferrari	1:16:42	225	
3	8	Palmer Zerbe	Ford	1:17:04	225	
4	22	Pete Hernandez	BMW	1:10:14	220	accident
5	12	José Marton	Chevrolet	1:12:56	220	overheated engine

66 Indirect Speech: Commands

"Take this pill."   **He told** me to take this pill.
"Don't forget it."   **He told** me not to forget it.

A. Student 1: read the command. Student 2: ask **Excuse me?** Student 1: report it as an indirect command. Use **said.**

   Ex. Please take your shoes off.
   Excuse me?
   I said to take your shoes off, please.

   1. Please come by a little early.
   2. Please don't send any flowers to the hospital.
   3. Please finish the homework before class.
   4. Please put sugar in my tea for me.
   5. Please don't drive so fast around this curve.
   6. Write an essay about an interesting experience of yours.
   7. Don't forget your doctor's appointment.

B. Report these commands. Use **told.**

   Ex. "Stay out of the fight, Ed," warned Milton.
   Milton told Ed to stay out of the fight.

   1. "Be back before midnight, kids," warned Mrs. Ching.
   2. "Clean the bird cage today, Sally," said Mr. Sandquist.
   3. "Don't get cigarette ashes on the furniture, Don," she said.
   4. "Don't smoke any more cigarettes, Mom," he begged.
   5. "May I have a 2:30 appointment, nurse?" Doreen asked.
   6. "Don't get too much sun, Mr. Walker," advised his doctor.
   7. "Duck your head, Ali!" Peggy cried.
   8. "Don't say another word on the subject, Jackie," Barbara said.
   9. "Move a little faster, soldier!" shouted the sergeant.

C. Report these instructions and commands. Use indirect speech.

   1. **The instructions say to remove the plastic wrapper.**

67 Linking Words

first	likewise	therefore	for example
finally	by the way	however	in other words

A. Fill in the blanks with linking words from the box above.

1. The baby deer got very weak. __Finally__, it died.
2. Alex Bright always leaves things on the bus. _____, he's very forgetful.
3. Don has worked at many jobs. _____, he was a salesman in his hometown.
4. Auto racing is expensive. _____, the special gasoline hose costs $1200.
5. I had a long visit with Marge Smith yesterday. _____, she sends you her regards.
6. We don't have money for a new car. _____, we hope this car lasts a couple of years.
7. Lenore didn't like biology in school. _____, she's working as a biologist now.
8. The oldest grandfather at the reunion will receive a book. _____, the youngest grandfather will receive something.

B. Put the sentences in the correct order. Use a linking word.

Ex. Ruth crashed the party. Ruth was an uninvited guest.
Ruth was an uninvited guest. In other words, she crashed the party.

1. Ms. Wan tried to get on the bus. The bus was full.
2. It was pouring rain. Mr. Ridgeway took his car.
3. I'm going to drink all the juice. I'm not going to leave any.
4. You don't have suntan lotion on. You can't stay in the sun very long.
5. This one has bigger leaves. Look at the difference between these bushes.
6. Ted's putting the model together. Ted's doing it the wrong way.
7. Careless campers cause a lot of fires. Lightning causes a lot of fires.
8. Neither team scored a goal for 55 minutes. The Eagles got a point.

C. Form two sentences. Use the linking word given.

1. therefore
The typewriter's not working right. Therefore, he can't finish the letter.
2. likewise
3. however
4. for example

1

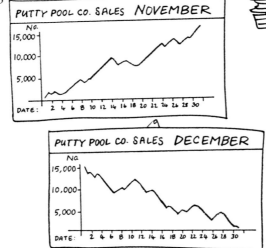

2

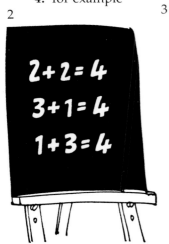

$2 + 2 = 4$
$3 + 1 = 4$
$1 + 3 = 4$

3

PUTTY POOL CO. SALES NOVEMBER

No.
15,000
10,000
5,000
DATE: 2 4 6 8 10 12 14 16 18 20 22 24 26 30

PUTTY POOL CO. SALES DECEMBER

No.
15,000
10,000
5,000
DATE: 2 4 6 8 10 12 14 16 18 20 22 24 26 30

4

HARRISON HIGH SCHOOL
JOB APPLICATION

Name Howard Jones

Address 497 Crescent Avenue
Beechwood, FL

Date of birth	Sex	Telephone #
4/9/59	M	391-4007

Previous Experience Substitute teacher at Morton High last year.

68 Two Relative Clauses

The mail **that came today** included a letter **that had postage due**.
The letter **(that) I got** has a stamp on it **(that) I want to keep**.

A. Form sentences. Begin with **the man that Evelyn married . . .** and match clauses 1–8 with relative clauses a–h.

1. works at the bank	a. that are hand sewn in Hong Kong
2. bought her a ring	b. that came to this country 300 years ago
3. drives a little car	c. that cost $5,000
4. comes from a family	d. that gives scholarships to orphans
5. has feet	e. that makes lamp shades
6. owns a company	f. that require special shoes
7. wears suits	g. that she has her account in
8. went to a college	h. that gets good mileage

1. **The man that Evelyn married works at the bank that she has her account in.**

_____

B. Fill in the blanks with the relative clauses in the correct order.

1. She got a computer **that talks** with the money **we gave her**. (that talks/we gave her)
2. This spray _____ will get rid of those insects _____. (I've brought/that are bothering you)
3. The woman _____ owns a horse _____. (that sat next to me/that won a prize in a horse show)
4. The Pat Smith _____ is a woman _____. (that has had many disappointments/you're talking about)
5. The doctor _____ treats people _____. (I'm recommending/that have heart trouble)
6. The tools _____ are in the truck _____. (that just left/we need)
7. This key _____ opens the closet _____. (we keep our supplies in/I'm giving you)
8. An animal _____ may have a shell _____. (that can't run fast/that will protect it)

_____

C. Student 1: read the question. Student 2: answer with **yes** and a full sentence. Use **one** or **ones** and relative clauses.

Ex. Does he have a dog that chases cars? (chases cats)
Yes, he has one that chases cars and one that chases cats.

1. Did he open an account that pays interest? (he can write checks on)
2. Are they sending a man that can fix typewriters? (can fix computers)
3. Does she have an ancestor that fought for the North in the Civil War? (fought for the South)
4. Will you stay at a place that has a swimming pool? (has free movies)
5. Does she listen to stations that play country music? (play classical music)
6. Did he collect stamps that honor famous generals? (show famous paintings)
7. Do you buy products that are advertised on TV? (my friends tell me about)

69 Two Clauses: Condition Clause and Another Clause

I'll pick you up **when you want to come home, if you call me.**
If you call me, I'll pick you up **when you want to come home.**

A. Form sentences. Begin with **if it rains, I'll cover the chairs . . .** and match 1–8 with clauses a–h to form adverb clauses.

1. as soon as
2. because
3. before
4. even though
5. if
6. so
7. where
8. while

a. you want me to cover them
b. you're taking the books inside
c. they get wet
d. they don't get wet
e. they're under a roof
f. they're not under a roof
g. water will ruin them
h. I can find a cover

1. If it rains, I'll cover the chairs as soon as I can find a cover.

B. Answer questions 1–8 with **yes** and a full sentence using an **if** clause with sentences a–h.

1. Do you drive when it snows?
2. Can we sit where we sat last time?
3. Can she sleep when the shades are up?
4. Will he move his car so Abdul can get by?
5. Do they charge extra when you dial a number?
6. Should we hurry home so the ice cream won't melt?
7. Will they clean the air filter when it needs it?
8. Do they play cards even though they always lose?

a. You reserve our seats early.
b. She asks him politely.
c. It's hot outside.
d. You talk to an operator.
e. He has snow tires on.
f. They're having fun.
g. It's a dark day.
h. You pay extra.

1. Yes, I drive when it snows, if I have snow tires on.

C. Student 1: read the question. Student 2: answer with **no, but** and a full sentence using the clause in parentheses. These are unreal conditions.

Ex. Did Connie pay the tax when it was due? (if she had known about it)
No, but she would have paid it when it was due, if she had known about it.

1. Did you look for the keys where the baby was playing? (if the baby had been playing with them)

2. Does she sing so everyone can hear her? (if she had a good voice)
3. Does he cry before the nurse gives him a shot? (if he saw the needle)
4. Can we eat while we're watching TV? (if you weren't eating watermelon)
5. Can Gina swim if she doesn't have a bathing cap? (if she had short hair)
6. Will they meet even though Daniel B. Cash isn't speaking? (if it were a regular monthly meeting)
7. Would you stay in the club if they raised the dues? (if they had more activities)

70 Two Clauses: Concession Clause and Another Clause

We stopped **when the time was up, although we weren't finished.**
Although we weren't finished, we stopped **when the time was up.**

A. Form sentences like the example. Use an **although** and a **when** clause.

> **Ex.** he has a lot of shoes/he always buys more/he gets a little money
> **Although he has a lot of shoes, he always buys more when he gets a little money.**

1. he had promised lower taxes/he had to raise taxes/he got in office

2. it's hot here/you'll need a sweater/you get to the ocean
3. the bridge was weak/the bridge didn't break/the truck drove over
4. the house isn't painted/I'll take a picture of the house/I get a roll of film
5. she's never played an instrument/she'll take clarinet lessons/she gets to high school
6. they usually give refunds/they don't give refunds/they're having a sale

---

B. Student 1: read the question. Student 2: answer with **yes, but** and a full sentence. Use **even though** and **because** clauses.

> **Ex.** Was the dam strong? (it broke/we had a week of heavy rain)
> **Yes, but even though it was strong it broke because we had a week of heavy rain.**

1. Was Mrs. Wu happy? (she cried/it was such a surprise)
2. Did he have an accident? (he wasn't hurt/he had his seat belt on)

3. Did Lois make a mistake in the figures? (her client didn't get upset/the mistake didn't affect the main points)
4. Did they drink some water? (they got thirsty again/they were working so hard)
5. Did you mail the letters yesterday? (they'll go out this morning/I missed the last pickup)
6. Does the company president like their soap? (they'll discontinue making it/it's not selling well)
7. Do you need to go to the dentist? (I won't go this week/I'm very busy)

C. Fill in the blanks with adverb subordinators. Use **even though** and one word from the list.

although	as soon as	before	if
until	when	while	so

1. Please don't go out __while__ it's raining **even though** you have a raincoat.
2. I'll lend you money _____ you can buy that stock _____ I don't recommend it.
3. _____ she was quite young at the time, she has a scar from _____ she fell off the bicycle.

4. _____ Mr. Armstrong liked teaching, he left that profession _____ he got an offer from a movie company.
5. _____ you want to, you can get there by tonight, _____ you're starting a little late.
6. _____ you have a reserved seat, you should get there _____ the show begins.
7. Take the pills _____ they're all gone _____ you already feel well.
8. _____ my aunt invited us, we won't visit her this year, _____ we'll be going near her house.

71 Two Clauses: Purpose Clause and Another Clause

I saved money **when my children were young so (that) they could go to college.**
When my children were young, I saved money **so (that) they could go to college.**

A. Form sentences starting with **I'll need**. Use a **when** and a **so** clause.

> Ex. traveler's checks/overseas/can get a refund easily.
> **I'll need traveler's checks when I go overseas so I can get a refund easily.**
>
> 1. a bag lunch/to work/don't have to eat out

2. my library card/to the library/can borrow some books
3. some stamps/on vacation/send my friends postcards
4. some suntan lotion/to the beach/don't get burned
5. a grocery list/to the supermarket/won't forget anything
6. warm clothes/to Quebec/will be comfortable
7. some change/downtown/can put it in the parking meter

B. Student 1: read the question. Student 2: answer with **yes** and a full sentence. Use an **even though** and a **so** clause.

> Ex. Will you give up candy? (I like it/I won't ruin my teeth)
> **Yes, even though I like it I'll give it up so I won't ruin my teeth.**
>
> 1. Will you practice today? (it's raining/I'll be ready for tomorrow's game)
> 2. Will Toshiro eat his kidney pie? (he doesn't like it/he won't displease his host)

3. Will Cecilia pick us up? (she doesn't have much time/we don't have to walk)
4. Have you thrown away the coffee? (it was still good/it wouldn't sit overnight)
5. Has Ron put more money in the parking meter? (there was some time left on it/he could go to the movie)
6. Did you pick the tomatoes? (they're not ripe/the birds won't get them)
7. Did Sue go to the marketing workshop? (she wasn't interested in it/she could increase her chances for a pay raise)

C. Fill in the blanks to complete the sentences. Use the information in parentheses to form an **if** clause and a **so (that)** clause.

> 1. **If they don't call us**, I'll call them **so that we can get started**. (we can get started/they don't call us)
> 2. _____, I'll give them a dollar _____. (they ask for a donation/they won't bother us anymore)
> 3. _____, I'll mow the lawn _____. (the grass doesn't get too high/the storm holds off a while longer)

4. _____, we'll change our strategy _____. (they'll have to change theirs/we lose sales to them)
5. _____, we'll reduce the price _____. (some books don't sell well/we can get them off the shelves)
6. _____, they'll give you an award _____. (you'll want to work 20 more years/you work there for 20 years)
7. _____, his doctor will prescribe something _____. (Mr. Hazlett gets a cold/Mr. Hazlett won't develop pneumonia)
8. _____, get me a sandwich _____. (I don't have to leave the office/you go out)

72 Included Relative Clause: In Relative Clause

I kept the flowers you had in the vase **she broke**.
I kept the flowers that were in the vase **that broke**.

A. Fill in the blanks with relative clauses.

1. This is the check **we wrote** for the sofa **we bought**. (we bought/we wrote)
2. These are some desserts _____ for the party _____. (I made/we're giving)
3. Do you have some paper _____ for an essay _____? (I can use/I'm writing)
4. Where are the flowers _____ by the tree _____? (they cut down/we planted)
5. What's the name _____ to the new cereal _____? (they're giving/they just developed)
6. Look at the marks _____ on the letter _____. (I typed/the dog made)
7. Is this the form _____ for the job _____? I'm applying for/I need)
8. Do you remember the pieces _____ at the performance _____? (you gave last summer/ you played)

B. Fill in the blanks to complete the sentences. Use two relative clauses.

1. Inez took a trip to New Guinea, and she wrote a book about it. Have you seen **the book (that) she wrote about the trip (that) she took?**
2. You brought some apples last week, and I made a pie with them. This is _____.
3. I lent you a book, and you tore a page out of it. Where's _____?
4. We cleaned out the files, and we found some important letters in them. These are _____.
5. We had a music festival last summer, and Eric designed the poster for it. Have you seen _____?
6. You gave me a large bottle, and I made a lamp out of it. Here's _____.
7. We already sent the package, and you put those things in it. What were _____?
8. I just painted this wall, and dirt has gotten on it. Look at _____.
9. You found a tea bag in the drawer, and you made tea with it. Is this _____?
10. We met a man on the subway, and we saw an unusual child with him. Do you remember _____?

C. Student 1: ask a yes/no question. Student 2: answer with **no** and a full sentence.

Ex. the dress that she made for the play that she was in//for the wedding she went to
Is this the dress that she made for the play that she was in?
No, it's the one she made for the wedding she went to.

1. the ring that she found in the ground that she dug up//in the box of things you sent over
2. the painting that you did during the week that you were home//on the weekend I went to the country
3. the reward that comes to people that work hard all their lives//to people that are lucky
4. the reason that's given to customers that ask for a refund//to people that ask silly questions
5. the name that he gave to the horse that he bought last year//to a ship he designed

73 Included Relative Clause: In Noun Clause

What you can do for people **who lose their houses** was the topic.
It's surprising how they helped people **who lost their houses**.

A. Form sentences like the example. Use the past continuous tense in the relative clause.

Ex. I/woman collect tolls/laugh
What I said to the woman who was collecting tolls made her laugh.

1. Mrs. Duncan/woman sit next to her/giggle
2. the bus driver/man sit in the back seat/smile
3. Marjorie/man fix her TV/angry
4. Mr. Hutchins/man watch him/frown
5. the teacher/the student chew gum/embarrassed
6. Miguel/the people tease him/furious
7. Lynn/man mow the park lawn/happy
8. Miss Whitney/the salesman call on the phone/angry
9. the nurse/the child cry/laugh
10. I/the neighbors have a noisy party/annoyed

B. Form sentences. Begin with **I haven't heard . . . .** Match noun clauses 1–8 with a **that** clause using a–h.

1. where Joyce got the book
2. how they made the kite
3. why they sold the house
4. where they took the car
5. what they know about the woman
6. when they'll reopen the stables
7. whether she'll enter the contest
8. whether Doug accepted the prize

a. they won the contest with
b. they lived in for so long
c. Channel 9 is holding
d. was in the accident
e. closed last month
f. used to live here
g. was out of print
h. he won

1. **I haven't heard where Joyce got the book that was out of print.**

C. Form a **yes/no** question. Begin with **wasn't it** and an adjective of your choice.

Ex. The truck fell into a ditch. See how they pulled it out.
Wasn't it unusual how they pulled out the truck that fell into a ditch?

1. The problem was worth ten extra points. See how Betty solved it.
2. They sent the package on Monday. See how quickly we got it.
3. He wore that shirt to the party. See how much money he paid for it.
4. Those footprints lead to the cabin. See where I found them.
5. These monkeys perform tricks. See what they feed them.
6. That woman sat next to him. This is what he asked her.
7. Her shoes had gotten wet. See where she dried them out.
8. The window was stuck. This is how she loosened it.
9. The man was traveling with five children. Here is why she helped him.

74 Included Relative Clause: In Adverb Clause

If you see a person **that fits that description**, call the police.
Before you buy a TV **that may not be as good**, check our prices.

A. Fill in the blanks to complete the sentences. Use an included relative clause introduced by the word in parentheses.

1. You may see a person that needs a place to sleep. (if) Refer him to the lodging office **if you see a person that needs a place to sleep**.
2. She admires a candidate that has a lot of experience in politics. (because)
She voted for Lorraine Mitchell _____.
3. There was a speech that was long and dull. (whenever)
We slipped out for a cup of coffee _____.

4. I drive on streets that have few stop signs. (when)
I get home fast _____.
5. They have a salesman that speaks Spanish. (if)
I'll shop there _____.
6. Winona took a course that trained her in physical therapy. (because)
Winona was a big help to her son _____.
7. Eating fruit and vegetables helps to keep you healthy. (because)
I recommend fresh fruit and vegetables _____.
8. You'll see a building that's being built. (where)
Turn left _____.

B. Answer questions 1–8 with an adverb clause a–h that includes a relative clause from s–z.

1. Why are you a little late?
2. Why do you like your neighbors?
3. When will you write him again?
4. Where will you wear your black suit?
5. Why do you read newspapers and books?
6. When will they give up the search?
7. How long have you grown tomatoes?
8. Why did they investigate the senator?
   1. **Because I took the bus that goes along Summit Avenue.**

a. Because I took the bus
b. When they find the gun
c. Where they require clothes
d. When he answers the letter
e. Because he accepted money
f. Since I moved to this house
g. Because they do a lot for people
h. Because I want to learn about things

s. that has room for a garden
t. that I wrote him last month
u. that goes along Summit Avenue
v. that a criminal offered him
w. that the robber used
x. that are more formal
y. that need their help
z. that will help me

C. Complete the sentences. Change the first sentence into a noun phrase modified by a relative clause.

1. Stephen got Marilyn a gift. Marilyn will be surprised when she opens **the gift that Stephen got her**.
2. The handles can break easily. Mrs. Huff won't buy those cups because they have _____.
3. The bouquet has a few red and yellow roses. I'll buy Mary some flowers if I see _____.
4. The food has hot spices in it. My aunt doesn't feel well after she eats _____.
5. The place is wet and muddy. I'd like to borrow your boots in case I have to work in _____.
6. The work is important. Marvin doesn't listen to music when he's doing _____.
7. Mr. Powell plays golf today. Mr. Powell won't be available today because this is _____.
8. The job lasts until 7 p.m. I always eat out when I have _____.
9. The teacher had five years experience. They didn't hire John because they were looking for _____.

75 Included Relative Clause: In Appositive

Harvey Kennedy, the **man who invented the shoelace**,
His hometown, a place **that no one has heard of**,

A. Form sentences with the given information. Begin with **I'm reading about . . . .**

Ex. Thomas Adams/inventor of chewing gum
I'm reading about Thomas Adams, the man who invented chewing gum.

1. Susan B. Anthony/leader of the suffragette movement
2. Leonardo da Vinci/painter of "Mona Lisa"
3. Marie Curie/discoverer of radium, winner of the Nobel Prize
4. Rudolf Diesel/inventor of the Diesel engine
5. Gertrude Ederle/swimmer of the English Channel
6. Catherine the Great/ruler of Russia from 1762 to 1796
7. Herman Melville/writer of *Moby Dick*
8. William Addis/inventor of the toothbrush
9. Harriet Tubman/organizer of the "Underground Railroad" to help slaves escape
10. Roald Amundsen/discoverer of the South Pole in 1911

B. Complete sentences 1–10 below by choosing from noun phrases a–j and relative clauses q–z.

a. a city
b. a fruit
c. a lawyer
d. a company
e. a fast game
f. a university
g. an exciting book
h. a southern state
i. an inexpensive car
j. a South American country

q. she knew from law school days
r. has excellent research facilities
s. is played in a closed court
t. gets excellent gas mileage
u. grows a lot of oranges
v. tells about hunting whales
w. I really wanted to see
x. makes office machines
y. I used to eat a lot
z. has no seacoast

1. She's at Stanford, <u>**a university that has excellent research facilities**</u>.
2. Phyllis drives a Subaru, _____.
3. I had to give up grapes, _____.
4. She hired Lee Coleman, _____.
5. Carlos is from Bolivia, _____.
6. I'm reading *Moby Dick* now, _____.
7. Orlando's a city in Florida, _____.
8. Chan's good at racketball, _____.
9. Chien Wu works for IBM, _____.
10. We didn't visit Brussels, _____.

Answer Key

UNIT 1 A: 2.16 other countries 3.Our other daughters 4.Several other states 5.My other clothes 6.some other trips 7.many other animals 8.No other team 9.No other city 10.your other suggestion **B:** 2.Three others 3.many others 4.some others/some other ones 5.Those others/Those other ones 6.my other/my other one 7.That other one 8.a few others/a few other ones 9.Those others/Those other ones 10.one other one **C:** Suggested answers: 2.My other ones 3.That other one 4.The others

UNIT 2 A: Suggested answers: 1.Most of the parks have an entrance fee. 2.Some of the parks have fishing. 3.A couple of the parks have guides. 4.Most of the parks have hiking. 5.None of the parks have/allow hunting. 6.All of the parks have picnic areas. 7.All of the parks have rest rooms. **B:** 2.many of her other ones 3.Most of the other ones 4.both of these others 5.any of the others 6.less of the other kind 7.both of her other ones 8.a lot of that other 9.All of my other students 10.a few of these other ones **C:** Suggested answers: 1.How many did she sell? She sold most of them. 2.How many did they win? They won 14 of them. 3.How many did you pass? I passed both of them. 4.How much did he keep for himself? He kept none of it. 5.How much do you sell? We sell all of it.

UNIT 3 A: Suggested answers: a seven-foot basketball player, a ten-ounce bottle of soda, a 15-gallon gasoline tank, a 25-pound sack of rice, a 32-story building, 90-degree temperature, a 2,000 mile airplane trip **B:** 1.Does she have a four-cylinder car? No, she has a six-cylinder car/one. 2.Did Mr. Marshall go to a seven-day conference? No, he went to a five-day conference/one. 3.Did the professor give a one-half hour lecture? No, he gave a two-hour lecture/one. 4.Is that a 40-passenger bus? No, it's a 50-passenger bus/one. 5.Is Jane reading a 200-page book? No, she's reading a 480-page book/one. 6.Are those three-quart pots? No, they're two-quart pots/ones. 7.Is that an 85-car freight train? No, it's a 100-car freight train/one. 8.Did she make a nine-minute call? No, she made a 20-minute call/one. 9.Did they use a 45-foot rope? No, they used a 30-foot rope/one. **C:** 2.A three-speed bicycle. 3.A ten-story building. 4.A 35-cent

candy bar. 5.A five-hour flight. 6.A six-lane highway.

UNIT 4 A: 2e. 3g. 4a. 51. 6d. 7j. 8k. 9i. 10b. 11h. 12c. **B:** Suggested answers: 1.She got a book about gardening from Ted. 2.She got two tickets to the theater from Maria. 3.She got a gift certificate for a sports store from Jim. 4.She got a box of candy from Miguel. 5.She got a make-up mirror for her dresser from Judy. 6.She got a weekend in New York from her parents. 7.She got a wristwatch with a second hand from her married sister. Suggested answers: 8.The one from Martha. The one from Maria. 9.The one from her parents. 10.The one from Jim. **C:** Suggested answers: I'd like to stay at the one near the stadium. (or) I'd like to stay at the one with the lowest rate.

UNIT 5 A: 2f. 3d. 4a. 5g. 6b. 7c. 8h. **B:** Suggested answers: 2.to say 3.to drink 4.to play 5.to spend 6.to eat 7.to wear 8.to rent 9.to take 10.to write **C:** 1.Is this a good place to keep my jewelry? No, but it's a good place to hide money. 2.Is this a good company to do business with? No, but it's a good company to work for. 3.Is Anne a good person to have on a hiking trip? No, but she's a good person to have on board a ship. 4.Is this good paper to draw pictures on? No, but it's good paper to type on. 5.Is this a good road to take to Springfield? No, but it's a good road/one to take to Athens. 6.Is this a good beach to swim at? No, but it's a good beach/one to look for shells on. 7.Is this a good movie to see on Halloween? No, but it's a good movie/one to stay away from. 8.Is this a good place to have the business meeting? No, but it's a good place to have the reception. 9.Is this the only time to see the art exhibit? No, but it's the only time to get in free. 10.Is this a good place to order seafood? No, but it's a good place to order steak.

UNIT 6 A: 2.the aching muscles in his back 3.his continuing wish to be a pilot 4.this half-finished report about coal 5.this well-written letter to the editor 6.a forgotten period of American history 7.Their 30-day trip to South America 8.her long-denied need to rest 9.Some singing birds by her window 10.a ten-pound baby boy with blue eyes 11.a shady spot under a tree

12.the remaining questions about the budget 13.an eight-lane highway to cross 14.the two-way radios in the cabs 15.many running horses with long tails 16.his bandaged arm to watch out for 17.The smoked fish at dinner 18.A packed theater for the first night 19.a good 30-second advertisement for Softie Soap 20.this round spoon with my name on it **B:** Suggested answers: 2.What was a stegosaurus? A bony-plated dinosaur with a terrible tail. 3.A three-horned, plant-eating dinosaur. 4.A 20-foot-tall, meat-eating dinosaur with a giant head.

UNIT 7 A: 2.the unusual 3.the suffering 4.the supernatural 5.the impossible 6.the curious 7.the innocent … the guilty 8.The weak … the strong **B:** 1.What do the unemployed need? They need jobs. 2.What do the poor need? They need financial help. 3.What do the elderly need? They need good medical treatment. 4.What do the overweight need? They need exercise. 5.What do the hungry need? They need food. 6.What do the sick need? They need medicine. 7.What do the hard of hearing need? They need hearing aids. **C:** 1.Only the rich can afford it. 2.They help the sick. 3.He tried to do the impossible. 4.She helped the wounded. 5.He stole from the rich. 6.He helped the poor.

UNIT 8 A: Suggested answers: 2.attractive, blue crystal lamps 3.plain, small, old rooms 4.large, round, white stones 5.beautiful, tiny, red flowers **B:** 2.big old blue 3.large brown leather 4.long dull pointless 5.clean modern office 6.small rectangular yellow 7.good inexpensive Spanish 8.short curly brown 9.long thin pale 10.short heavy old **C:** Suggested answers: 2.an old, brave captain 3.some beautiful little flowers 4.a terrible, ugly, wild monster.

UNIT 9 A: Suggested answers: 2es. 3bv. 4fw. 5gu. 6cz. 7hy. 8dx. **B:** Suggested answers: 1.What's a raincoat? It's a coat that will keep the rain off you. 2.What are address books? They're books that you can keep your friends' addresses in. 3.What's a dictionary? It's a book that gives the spelling, pronunciation, and meaning of words. 4.What are photocopying machines? They're machines that copy printed material. 5.What's a wristwatch? It's a watch that you wear on your wrist. 6.What's a freezer? It's a machine that keeps food frozen. 7.What's typing paper? It's paper that you can type on. 8.What are life insurance policies? They're policies that pay your family money when you die. 9.What's a drive-in bank window? It's a bank window that you can reach from your car. **C:** Suggested answers: If you went shopping today, which gloves would you buy? I'd buy the ones that are for driving. If you went shopping today, which camera would you buy? I'd buy the one that has the zoom lens included.

UNIT 10 A: 2e.The days that are so hot and humid. 3a.The roads that go through the center of town. 4c.The plants that grow in the desert. 5d.The bank teller that always waits on me. 6j.The road that has holes in it. 7f.The shoes that got wet on the porch. 8i.The company that's losing money. 9b.The doctor that performed the operation. 10h.The birds that glide long distances. **B:** 1.Did they find the car that was used in the bank robbery? No, they found the one that was used in the jewelry store robbery. 2.Was Westwood the town that lowered its property tax? No, it was the one that lowered its school tax. 3.Will you punish the kids that played on the front lawn? No, I'll punish the ones that ran through the flower garden. 4.Is Doris Clendening the person that handles your insurance policy? No, she's the one that handles my travel arrangements. 5.Does he want to marry a woman that can hike 25 miles a day? No, he wants to marry one that can cook good spaghetti. 6.Did they buy the house that had four bedrooms? No, they bought the one that had the big backyard. 7.Did José go to an optician that graduated from George Washington University? No, he went to one that studied in Europe. 8.Is your sister seeing a young man that works in her office? No, she's seeing one that comes from Maine. 9.Does Meg Powell go to stores that have the cheapest prices? No, she goes to ones that carry imported items. **C:** Suggested answers: 2.A girl that wears her hair in long braids. 3.A chicken that has four feet. 4.A horseman that had no head.

UNIT 11 A: 2d. 3a. 4g. 5c. 6h. 7i. 8j. 9b. 10f. **B:** 1.It's the Sears Tower, which is 110 stories high. 2.It was the Battle of Waterloo, which took place in 1815. 3.She was born on January 24, which turned out to be the coldest day of the winter. 4.The Clover Company, which

makes paint. 5.It was Marisol Martinez, who sells insurance. 6.She married David Shepson, who is rapidly becoming a famous opera star. 7.They got married in 1984, which was an important election year. **C:** Suggested answers: 2.who walked on the moon 3.which are the tallest trees in the world 4.who is the new head of the Supreme Court

UNIT 12 A: 2.which is black and white 3-4.who'll be assigned to Africa 5-6.who speak some French 7-8.which needs technical aid **B:** Suggested answers: 1.who is an insurance agent 2.whose maiden name was Knapp 3.who is an insurance agent 4.who was born in 1908 … who was a mill worker 5.who is Kathy's grandmother … who became an insurance agent **C:** 2j.(no commas) 3h.(no commas) 4i.(commas) 5e.(commas) 6f.(comma) 7d.(commas) 8a.(no commas) 9b.(commas) 10g.(no commas)

UNIT 13 A: 2f.A car costing over $15,000 is much too expensive. 3d.The baby crawling on the floor almost tripped me. 4j.Does she have any relatives living in Poland? 5a.Do you know that young woman coming out of the elevator? 6b.Everybody not having a free ticket must pay the admission. 7h.She took a picture of some birds feeding their young. 8e.A policeman spoke to some children playing in the street. 9g.Why don't you throw away that bike rusting in the yard? 10i.I tried to get the attention of the waiter serving our table. **B:** 2cv. 3hs. 4iz. 5ax. 6gr. 7eq. 8dw. 9bt. 10fy. **C:** 2.A plant producing medicine. 3.A magazine telling about karate. 4.A burglar holding a money bag.

UNIT 14 A: 3j.Juanita carried the books needed for her computer course home. 4i.The math problems marked with a red x are wrong. 5g.The tree struck by lightning had to be cut down. 6h.They're putting tickets on the cars parked on that side. 7b.The thief entered through a gate not locked by the night guard. 8f.Many books intended for children have colorful pictures. 9c.Children raised on a vegetarian diet have protein deficiencies. 10e.Anne's credit cards, stolen from her purse, haven't been returned. **B:** 2.thrown … cut 3.injured/hurt 4.dazed 5.injured/hurt 6.broken 7.demolished

UNIT 15 A: 1.Water running over rocks … 2.Milk not kept in the refrigerator …

3.A loaded gun … 4.The lady collecting the invitations … 5.Book reports not typed … 6.Claire's smiling face … 7. … several questions answered at the meeting. 8.The people searching for the skiers … 9. … the lost skiers … **B:** 2h.The leaking ones. 3c.The one having the best safety record. 4b.The one paying only five percent interest. 5d.The one leading to a back room. 6j.The flashing ones. 7g.The ones coming in last. 8i.The decayed one. 9a.The ones packed in my suitcase. 10f.The ones made of plastic. [Note: The drill can be done again using a *that* clause—The one that was sent by Express Mail.] **C:** Suggested answers: 2.A car stuck in the mud. (or) A stuck car. 3.An injured tennis player. (or) A tennis player injured playing a game. 4.A burning stable.

UNIT 16 A: Suggested answers: 1.Is editing books an exciting job? No, but designing books is. 2.Is playing tennis difficult for you? Yes, but playing golf isn't. 3.Is answering the office telephone part of your job? No, but helping the doctor is. 4.Is developing pictures fun? No, but taking pictures is. 5.Is cutting hair hard? No, but styling hair is. 6.Is studying math entertaining? Yes, but studying English isn't. 7.Is acting his ambition in life? No, but directing a movie is. [Note: The drill can also be done using a verb other than *be*—Does fixing radios take a lot of training? No, but fixing TVs does.] **B:** 1.What did going to Westfield accomplish? Not much, but calling up the company's representative helped. 2.What did studying French grammar accomplish? Not much, but practicing in the language lab helped. 3.What did reading books about exercise programs accomplish? Not much, but doing some actual exercises helped. 4.What did blaming Mr. Meadows accomplish? Not much, but looking for my own mistakes helped. 5.What did yelling at the child accomplish? Not much, but talking to her quietly helped. 6.What did wiping the grease spot with a paper towel accomplish? Not much, but washing it with soap and water helped. 7.What did not drinking coffee accomplish? Not much, but not smoking cigarettes helped. 8.What did not complaining about the air conditioning accomplish? Not much, but turning on a fan helped. 9.What did refusing to pay the rent accomplish? Not much, but petitioning the rent board helped. 10.What did mentioning Jessica's name accomplish? Not much, but writing an impressive resumé helped. **C:** 2d.Winning the game 3b.Finishing school 4c.Being assertive 5a.Finding a ticket 6e.Riding a horse

UNIT 17 A: 2.He'd rather eat dessert, but he'd better eat his meat and vegetables. 3.He'd rather watch TV, but he'd better do his homework. 4.She'd rather play baseball, but she'd better practice her oboe. **B:** 1.Dan Stebbins would rather not shovel the snow now, but he'd better. He'd better not wait any longer. 2.Connie would rather not have the operation, but she'd better. She'd better not worry about the cost. 3.Tom would rather not see the doctor yet, but he'd better. He'd better not delay another day. 4.Marie would rather not quit smoking, but she'd better. She'd better not ruin her health. 5.Valerie Jones would rather not eat breakfast today, but she'd better. She'd better not go to work on an empty stomach. 6.Kevin would rather not wear hiking boots, but he'd better. He'd better not wear sneakers on the hike. 7.They'd rather not go to bed now, but they'd better. They'd better not stay up until 2 a.m. again. 8.My sister would rather not follow the doctor's orders, but she'd better. She'd better not eat any salty foods. 9.Steve would rather not talk to Ms. Stone, but he'd better. He'd better not act without her advice.
C: Suggested answers: 1.Do the hikers want to go on to the next station, or would they rather camp here? I think they'd rather camp here. 2.Do your children want to go swimming, or would they rather play a video game? I think they'd rather go swimming. 3.Does Greg want to plan the family budget, or would he rather talk on the phone? I think he'd rather plan the family budget. 4.Does Luz want to buy a new foreign car, or would she rather keep her old car a while longer? I think she'd rather buy a new one. 5.Does Chuck want to go on the picnic, or would he rather stay home and watch the house? I think he'd rather go on the picnic. 6.Does the taxi driver want to pick up one more fare, or would he rather quit work for the day? I think he'd rather pick up one more fare. 7.Does the Atlas Company want to enlarge their factory, or would they rather merge with Herculoids Inc.? I think they'd rather enlarge their factory.

UNIT 18 A: 1.No, but they'll have a carnival. 2.No, but he may play

volleyball. 3.No, but we should eat a lot of natural fibers. 4.No, but they must sign them. 5.No, but it might get stuck. 6.No, but he can leave a little later. 7.No, but you should invest in real estate. 8.No, but he could say the alphabet. 9.No, but I'll enter the 5,000 meter race. **B:** 2.but she wasn't allowed to last year 3.but they didn't have to last year 4.but she wasn't able to last year 5.but she wasn't willing to last year 6.but he didn't have to last year 7.but it wasn't good for them to go last year 8.but they weren't likely to accept one last year **C:** Suggested answers: 1.She must be able to read and write French well. 2.We'll have to use the side entrance. 3.He might be able to use a credit card. 4.He should be able to speak Spanish now. 5.We shouldn't have to pay any more. 6.She shouldn't be allowed to stay up until midnight. 7.She won't be able to finish her science project. 8.It might be dangerous for him to go out in this bad weather. 9.It will be wise for them to take traveler's checks. 10.It won't be possible for us to change seats now.

UNIT 19 A: Suggested answers: 1.Will she have raised the children by 1990? No, and she won't even have raised them by 1995. 2.Will Karen have finished her schooling by 1990? Yes, she will have finished it in 1989. 3.Will they have paid off their loan by 1990? No, and they won't even have paid it off by 1995. 4.Will interest rates have gone down to five percent by next year? No, and they won't even have gone down by the year after. 5.Will space stations have become common by 1990? No, and they won't even have become common by 1995. 6.Will Pierre have learned English by next year? Yes, he will have learned it by next year. 7.Will Westwood have built the planetarium by 1990? No, and they won't even have built it by 1995. 8.Will the highway department have completed the project by 1990? Yes, they will have completed it in 1988. 9.Will someone have found a cure for colds by the year 2000? No, and they won't even have found one by the year 2010. **B:** 1.Not then. But we must have located her before 5 p.m. 2.Not then. But they can have begun it before August 15. 3.Not then. But he should have finished it before the tenth of the month. 4.Not then. But we must have doubled them before March 31. 5.Not then. But he could have passed it before the end of March. 6.Not then. But we should have cleared it with him before the conference. 7.Not then. But

you should have paid it before the end of the year. 8.Not then. But he must have signed it before tomorrow.
C: 1.How long will it have been since their first message? 2.Where will you have traveled by the end of your trip? 3.How many days will you have been on the road by the end of your trip? 4.How many interviews will the reporter have conducted by December 31? 5.How much medicine will Mark have taken by Friday? 6.How tall will Al have grown by the time we see him again? 7.How long will Ruth have worked at this plant by the time she retires? 8.What will Alessandra have learned about the machine by the end of the training course? 9.Which runners will have crossed the finish line after two hours?

UNIT 20 A: 1.Yes, they must have helped them. 2.Yes, they may have been the cause of it. 3.Yes, they could have traveled at night. 4.Yes, he might have entered there. 5.Yes, he must have gotten tired. 6.Yes, he might have told her that. 7.Yes, she could have been on it. **B:** 1.Where could the cat have hidden her kittens? 2.Who might have seen the thief? 3.What would a nurse have done in that situation? 4.What may have caused the power failure? 5.Which pilot could have seen the other plane first? 6.How long should this cake have been in the oven? 7.How many matches could Nancy have won in 20 years? 8.When should the planning board have changed their decision? 9.How could the police officer have made such a mistake? **C:** 1.She must not have filed it correctly. 2.They must not have made the payments. 3.He might not have hung it up there. 4.He shouldn't have lost. 5.I might not have lost it. 6.He couldn't have beaten him, though. 7.They couldn't have fixed it properly. 8.She couldn't have forgotten about that.

UNIT 21 A: 1.Would you have done that? No, I would have taken it to the lost and found. 2.No, I would have gotten it fixed. 3.No, I would have known the answer. 4.No, I would have written it myself. 5.No, I would have kept them. 6.No, I would have just had a snack. 7.No, I would have left the room. 8.No, I would have waited for a green light. 9.No, I would have complained to the manager. **B:** 1.He shouldn't have taken the car. He should have taken the subway. 2.He shouldn't have bet on the horse race.

He should have bet on the lottery. 3.You shouldn't have worn a sweater. You should have worn a parka. 4.You shouldn't have joined the army. You should have joined the navy. 5.She shouldn't have written a novel. She should have written poetry.
C: Suggested answers: 1.Where could/ might he have lost it? Well, he could have lost it at the ball game. 2.What kind might she have bought? Well, she might have bought "La Fragrance." 3.When might she have gone? Well, she might have gone on the 9:30 plane. 4.Where could he have been? Well, he could have been in Oliver's office. 5.How much could you have paid for it? Well, I could have paid about $8,000. 6.Who should he have told? Well, he should have told his family. 7.What should she have tried to win? Well, she should have tried to win the ice cream-making contest. 8.Where should they have gone? Well, they should have gone to the main administration building. 9.What might she have gone there for? Well, she might not have been feeling well.

UNIT 22 A: 1.She shouldn't have been buying gold. She should have been buying silver. 2.They shouldn't have been working. They should have been going on vacation. 3.We shouldn't have been watching Carrie/her. We should have been watching Marta. 4.She shouldn't have been standing. She should have been lying down. 5.He shouldn't have been driving a sports car. He should have been driving an economy car. 6.They shouldn't have been playing in the street/there. They should have been playing on the sidewalk. 7.They shouldn't have been hiring more secretaries. They should have been hiring more drivers. 8.She shouldn't have been burning the newspapers. She should have been keeping them. 9.It shouldn't have been reducing its advertising. It should have been increasing it. **B:** 2f.She must have been eating a lot of candy. 3b.He could have been wearing a disguise. 4e.She might have been trying to call us. 5d.They might have been having an argument. 6a.He should have been waiting inside. 7g.They must have been running hard. 8c.It might have been delivering furniture. **C:** 2.In 1990, will he have been working for 40 years? Yes, he will have. 3.On Tuesday, will they have been traveling for ten weeks? Yes, they will have. 4.By 9:30, will they have been boxing for half an hour? No, they won't have.

UNIT 23 A: 1.He must not have been disciplined. 2.She must not have been told. 3.They might not have been fed. 4.It might not have been checked over. 5.He might not have been injured badly. 6.It couldn't have been paid. 7.It couldn't have been curled. 8.It can't have been fixed. 9.It can't have been changed recently. **B:** 1.Should they have been set two feet apart? No, they should have been set four feet apart. 2.Should they have been paid yesterday? No, they should have been paid last week. 3.Should he have been fired last week? No, he should have been fired last year. 4.Should they have been ordered recently? No, they should have been ordered a long time ago. 5.Should it have been painted? No, it should have been repaired first. 6.Should it have been watered? No, it should have been cut first. 7.Should it have been treated? No, it should have been x-rayed first. 8.Should he/she have been fed? No, he/she should have been bathed first. 9.Should the book have been put on the library shelves? No, it should have been cataloged first. **C:** Suggested answers: 2.How many miles will have been flown in the year 2000? Thirty-one million. 3.How many hamburgers will have been served by the year 2000? Thirty-four million will have been served. 4.How much money will have been earned in the year 2000? Four thousand, four hundred dollars will have been earned.

UNIT 24 A: 1.Tom hasn't been working hard. He's been taking it easy. 2.Teresa hasn't been cutting hair. She's been giving shampoos. 3.Ari and Peggy haven't been watching the movie. They've been eating popcorn. 4.The company hasn't been using the old brushes. They've been throwing them away. 5.The judge hasn't been listening to the witness. He's/She's been writing something. 6.His wife hasn't been saving money for the future. She's been buying lottery tickets. 7.The cat hasn't been hunting mice. It's been sleeping on the sofa. 8.Jerry hasn't been cooking the steaks. He's been playing horseshoes. 9.Those artists haven't been painting pictures. They've been sitting around. 10.Keith hasn't been working overtime. He's been going home early. **B:** 1.Paul's been playing in the mud, and Mike has too. 2.Amin's been losing support, and his partner has too. 3.She's been keeping a secret, and he has too. 4.We've been borrowing money, and the Finches have too. 5.Juan's been buying Safeco stock, and Maggie has

too. 6.They've been hiring engineers, and we have too. 7.Our doctor's been charging more, and our dentist has too. 8.Ed's been using language tapes, and Valerie has too. 9.You've been working hard, and your husband has too. **C:** 2.Henry has been playing golf, and Maria has been playing tennis. 3.Mr. Ramos has been cooking chicken, and Mercedes has been painting the house. 4.Patty has been talking on the phone, and Mark has been typing.

UNIT 25 A: 1.What's Mr. Garcia been doing recently? He's been working in Chicago. How long has he been doing that/working there? For several months. 2.What's Henry been doing recently? He's been working at the King Automobile Factory. How long has he been doing that/working there? Since last year. 3.What has Dr. Ferguson been doing recently? He's been attending some conferences. Where has he been attending them? In Brazil and France. 4.... She's been looking for a new job.... 5.... He's been studying creative writing.... 6.She's been studying in Paris.... 7.... He's been studying Chinese.... 8.... She's been writing a novel.... **B:** The work force has been falling. Sales have been rising. The debt has been falling. **C:** 2.been dating ... hasn't 3.hasn't been making ... has 4.have been barking ... haven't 5.has been running ... hasn't 6.have been changing ... haven't 7.hasn't been drinking ... has 8.hasn't been making ... has 9.hasn't been melting ... has 10.has been bringing ... hasn't 11.have been broadcasting ... haven't 12.haven't been appearing ... have

UNIT 26 A: 1.No, she's been working on it for several days, but she hasn't finished it yet. 2.No, I've been working on them for over a week, but I haven't sent them in yet. 3.No, she's been looking for it for several days, but she hasn't found it yet. 4.No, they've been planning that trip for a year, but they haven't gone yet. 5.No, he's been planning to do it for two weeks, but he hasn't returned it yet. 6.No, they've been advertising it for six months, but they haven't sold it yet. 7.No, he's been fishing for three or four hours, but he hasn't caught any fish yet. 8.No, they've been playing for two and a half months, but they haven't won many yet. 9.No, he's been considering her for a while, but he hasn't hired her yet. 10.No, I've been getting ready to do it for a week, but I haven't done it yet. 11.No, she's been buying newsstand copies for a year, but she hasn't subscribed to it yet. 12.No, he's been looking for one for two months, but he hasn't found one yet. **B:** 2.has been shopping 3.has never seen 4.has been snowing 5.hasn't rained 6.have known 7.have been calling 8.has blown 9.hasn't been writing 10.has gone 11.have been building … has cost 12.have been watching … has happened

UNIT 27 A: 1.No, he'd already eaten. 2.No, the dealer had already sold it. 3.No, it had already left. 4.No, he'd already corrected them. 5.No, the bell had already rung. 6.No, the chef had already cooked it. 7.No, someone had already bought it. 8.No, he'd already reported it. 9.No, they'd already locked the door. **B:** 1.Hadn't he ever bet on one before? 2.Hadn't she ever driven it before? 3.Hadn't she ever sung a solo before? 4.Hadn't you ever read it before? 5.Hadn't you ever seen it before? 6.Hadn't you ever tasted his chocolate cake before? 7.Hadn't you ever heard it before? 8.Hadn't she ever worn it before? 9.Hadn't they ever tried it before? **C:** Suggested answers: 2.Patrick had not yet graduated from high school 3.Patrick had not yet become a reporter 4.Rudy had already gone to Vietnam 5.Rudy had already become a sergeant 6.Sarah had already been a manager at Loft's for five years

UNIT 28 A: 2.hadn't been earning 3.hadn't been locking 4.had been giving 5.had been playing 6.hadn't been attracting 7.had been investing 8.had been burning 9.hadn't been turning in 10.had been bothering **B:** Suggested answers: Had Brian been getting up at 5:30 before the meet? Yes, he had. (or) Had Brian been getting up at 5:00 every morning? No, he hadn't. He'd been getting up at 5:30. (or) Had Brian been having heavy breakfasts? No, he hadn't. He'd been having light ones. **C:** 2.Where had the boys been swimming? They'd been swimming in a no swimming area. 3.What had the boy been eating? He'd been eating chocolate. 4.How long had the store been open? It'd been open for four years.

UNIT 29 A: 2.lost/had lost 3.was throwing/had been throwing 4.has been bending 5.had been aching 6.have been having 7.were carrying 8.have … spent 9.was reading … knocked 10.did … see … have … seen 11.have … read 12.had … played … played … has

played **B:** Suggested answers: 2.She has been buying apples. 3.He's been selling fruits. 4.He's been throwing away a soda can. 5.He's been drinking soda. 6.She's been cleaning.

UNIT 30 A: The Apollo 11 moon rocket was launched on July 17, 1969. The (U.S.) bicentennial was celebrated across the country on July 4, 1976. The airlines were struck by the air traffic controllers on August 3, 1981. (President) Reagan was re-elected by a landslide on November 6, 1984. Thousands (of people) were hurt in a chemical accident in Bhopal, India on December 3, 1984. Mexico City was hit with/by a major earthquake on September 19, 1985. The U.S.-U.S.S.R. summit was opened in Geneva on November 19, 1985. Seven astronauts were killed in the (space shuttle) Challenger explosion on January 28, 1986. New lows were reached for oil prices on May 5, 1986. **B:** 1.Why did they wash this floor? It wasn't washed; it was swept. 2.Why did they shoot the beavers? They weren't shot; they were trapped. 3.Why did they keep old newspapers? They weren't kept; they were thrown away. 4.Why do they slice the apples at the cannery? They aren't sliced; they're peeled. 5.Why do they spend all their money on clothes? It isn't (all) spent on clothes; it's invested in stocks. 6.Why did they cancel today's game? It wasn't canceled; it was postponed. 7.Why do they throw out the sour milk? It isn't thrown out; it's used in cooking. 8.Why do they type those formal invitations? They aren't typed; they're written by hand. 9.Why did they take the case to court? It wasn't taken to court; it was settled out of court. 10.Why did they throw away all the old books? They weren't thrown away; they were sold. **C:** 2.was taken … He wasn't taken to jail. 3.was stolen … It wasn't stolen on Monday. 4.were broken … They weren't broken by hail. 5.was baked … It wasn't baked yesterday. 6.was hit … He/She wasn't hit by a car. 7.is raised … It isn't raised at 8 a.m. 8.were paid … We weren't paid on February 26.

UNIT 31 A: 1.In 1610, Galileo discovered Jupiter's four largest moons. Jupiter's four largest moons were discovered by Galileo in 1610. 2.In 1648, Shah Jehan finished the Taj Mahal. The Taj Mahal was finished by Shah Jehan in 1648. 3.In 1774, Joseph Priestly discovered oxygen. Oxygen was discovered by Joseph Priestly in

1774. 4.In 1808, Beethoven completed his Fifth Symphony. Beethoven's Fifth Symphony was completed in 1808. 5.In 1814, Francis Scott Key wrote "The Star Spangled Banner." "The Star Spangled Banner" was written by Francis Scott Key in 1814. 6.In 1823, Clement Moore wrote "Visit from St. Nicholas." "Visit from St. Nicholas" was written by Clement Moore in 1823. 7.In 1863, Abraham Lincoln signed the Emancipation Proclamation. The Emancipation Proclamation was signed by Abraham Lincoln in 1863. 8.In 1867, the United States bought Alaska from Russia. Alaska was bought from Russia (by the United States) in 1867. 9.In 1872, Thomas Adams invented chewing gum. Chewing gum was invented by Thomas Adams in 1872. 10.In 1875, Bizet completed *Carmen*. *Carmen* was completed by Bizet in 1875. 11.In 1903, the Wright brothers made the first airplane flight. The first airplane flight was made by the Wright brothers in 1903. 12.In 1905, Albert Einstein formulated the theory of relativity. The theory of relativity was formulated by Albert Einstein in 1905. 13.In 1935, Carl McGee invented the parking meter. The parking meter was invented by Carl McGee in 1935. 14.In 1949, George Orwell wrote the novel *Nineteen Eighty-Four*. The novel *Nineteen Eighty-Four* was written by George Orwell in 1949. 15.In 1954, Roger Bannister ran the first four-minute mile. The first four-minute mile was run by Roger Bannister in 1954. 16.In 1964, the Nobel prize committee awarded the peace prize to Martin Luther King, Jr. Martin Luther King, Jr. was awarded the peace prize by the Nobel prize committee in 1964. 17.In 1967, Dr. Christiaan Barnard performed the first human heart transplant. The first human heart transplant was performed by Dr. Christiaan Barnard in 1967. 18.In 1982, Italy won the World Cup in soccer. The World Cup in soccer was won by Italy in 1982. **B:** Ted: like … spent … were invited … have … see Jody: got … was tied up … move … was postponed … visited Ted: read … was built.

UNIT 32 A: 1.Is the cash counted at the front window? No, it isn't. 2.Are the buses washed every week? Yes, they are. 3.Is the money invested in real estate? No, it isn't. 4.Is grain grown in the Midwest? Yes, it is. 5.Are passenger cars manufactured in this factory? Yes, they are. 6.Are 30 cars sold every week? No, they aren't. 7.Are the church bells rung on Saturday? No, they aren't. 8.Are children admitted free on Tuesdays and Thursdays? Yes, they are. 9.Are tourists invited to the fort on Saturdays? No, they aren't. B: Suggested answers: 2.Was the ditch dug by hand? No, it was dug by an excavator. 3.Was the play attended by a lot of people? No, it was attended by a few people. 4.Was the room painted by a roller? No, it was painted by a brush. C: 1.No, it was installed yesterday. 2.No, they were delivered to the wrong address. 3.No, it's kept in the bottom drawer. 4.No, it was knit by my grandmother. 5.No, they were fed at noon. 6.No, he was hit by a snowball. 7.No, they're sold at our other store. 8.No, it was spent on several buildings. 9.No, they were taught two years ago.

UNIT 33 A: 1.Who were they made by? 2.Who was he hired by? 3.Who were they burned by? 4.Who was he/she saved by? 5.Who were they given a loan by? 6.Who was it written by? 7.Who were they fed by? 8.Who were they amused by? [Note: This drill can be done again using the more formal *whom*. It can also be done with another student supplying an answer for the question. In #8 the collective noun *audience* takes the singular verb *was* in the statement, but the plural pronoun *they* in the question.] B: 1.Where are aluminum cans collected? 2.When were the brakes checked? 3.When was the music program started? 4.When were the hotel reservations made? 5.Where were the emeralds sold? 6.Where was the other hiker found? 7.When was the inside painted? 8.When are the monkeys fed? C: The book was written by Jeremy Harben. It was published in 1987. It was printed in the United States of America. The cover was designed by Akiko Pei. The pictures were drawn by Fred Wilson. The first printing was made in July of 1987.

UNIT 34 A: 2c.They aren't being hired yet. 3f.They aren't being left in the mailbox. 4b.It isn't being fried. 5a.He isn't being arrested. 6e.He/She wasn't being interviewed. 7g.They weren't being sold. 8d.He/She wasn't being ignored. B: 2.Is her hair being cut? No, it's being washed. 3.Is the shirt being washed? No, it's being ironed. C: 1.Was a new office being built? Yes, it was. Who was it being built by? (It was being built) By the Fargo Construction Company. 2.Is the winning horse being photographed? Yes, it is. Who is it being photographed

by? (It's being photographed) By the fans. 3.Are the dead batteries being replaced? Yes, they are. Who are they being replaced by? (They are being replaced) By Mr. Trapp. 4.Are the votes being counted? Yes, they are. Who are they being counted by? (They're being counted) By the election committee. 5.Was the art exhibit being financed? Yes, it was. Who was it being financed by? (It was being financed) By the Milo Foundation. 6.Were the foreign news reporters being entertained? Yes, they were. Who were they being entertained by? (They were being entertained) By the senator. 7.Is the new union being opposed? Yes, it is. Who is it being opposed by? (It's being opposed) By some truck drivers. 8.Is a soccer field being constructed there? Yes it is. Who is it being constructed by? (It's being constructed) By the Department of Parks. 9.Was a protest being planned? Yes, it was. Who was it being planned by? (It was being planned) By a small group of taxpayers.

UNIT 35 A: 2.he was promised 3.she isn't allowed 4.I was given 5.they weren't taught 6.I wasn't offered 7.She was helped 8.She was given 9.we were sent 10.He wasn't told B: 1.The Joneses were billed $95. 2.Oliver was sent a nice birthday card. 3.Ling was trained in proofreading. 4.Scientists are shown the research labs. 5.The audience is given the answer. 6.The older children are read mystery stories. 7.His mother was told another story. 8.The entree was made this morning. 9.Perishable items are shipped by air. 10.The index is/was typeset last. [Note: Sentences 2, 4-7 can also be done using the direct object as subject of the passive sentence—A nice birthday card was sent to Oliver.] C: 2.The elephant is being fed peanuts. 3.The lion is being fed meat. 4.The seals are being fed fish. 5.The gorilla is being fed bananas. 6.The giraffe is being fed leaves.

UNIT 36 A: 1.What has been pulled out of the magician's hat? 2.Who has Phil been interviewed by? 3.Where have his fingerprints been found? 4.How has the name of the winner been learned? 5.When had that tool been invented? 6.Which doctors had the men been checked by? 7.How long have these products been used? B: 1.He has been kidnapped. 2.I have been delayed this morning. 3.They had been hidden in a cave. 4.She has been given a scholarship there. 5.It had been

weakened on the inside. 6.It had been stolen. 7.It hadn't been stolen. 8.We haven't been invited. C: Have the spark plugs been replaced? No, they haven't. Has the oil filter been changed? Yes, it has. Have the tires been rotated? No, they haven't. Have the drive belts been adjusted? No, they haven't. Has a new muffler been installed? No, it hasn't. Has the timing been checked? Yes, it has.

UNIT 37 A: 1.His electric bill won't be paid this week, but his phone bill will (be). 2.This lock can't be forced, but that one can (be). 3.A first-class ticket can be refunded, but an economy-class ticket can't (be). 4.The sales tax should be reduced, but the gasoline tax shouldn't (be). 5.Professor Gross shouldn't be retired, but Professor Sawyer should (be). 6.The ceiling would be damaged, but the walls wouldn't (be). 7.The hockey game will be canceled, but the ski jumping contest won't (be). 8.The stolen money might be found, but the robbers might not (be). 9.The governor will be invited, but the president won't (be). 10.The mirrors won't be sent by truck, but the chairs will (be). 11.This wine shouldn't be drunk right away, but this milk should (be). B: 1.Should it be bandaged with a cloth? Yes, it should (be). 2.Will he be sent to prison soon? Yes, he will (be). 3.Can it be finished before dark? No, it can't (be). 4.Will it be sent up to Mars? No, it won't (be). 5.Can they be turned out now? Yes, they can (be). 6.Can it be taken in the car? Yes, it can (be). 7.Will it be solved by a child? No, it won't (be). C: Suggested answers: 2.How many windows should be washed? Most of them should (be). 3.Who might be chosen as the winner? Miss Montana might (be). 4.Must the tree be removed? Yes it must (be).

UNIT 38 A: 1.He's practiced not using a cane. 2.I've decided not to take any more physics courses. 3.You're risking not getting enough vitamin C. 4.He managed not to wake up his wife. 5.They enjoy not studying every day. 6.I'm considering not sending Christmas cards this year. 7.They've learned not to look at the keyboard. 8.Promise not to spend more than $15. 9.I'll miss not seeing her every day. [Note: In the reply, students should give sentence stress (contrastive stress) to the word *not*.] B: 1.Did she pretend to be a student? No, she pretended not to be one. 2.Did they decide to use the elevator? No, they decided not to use it. 3.Do you suggest taking an extra suitcase? No, I suggest not taking (an extra) one. 4.Did they agree to share expenses? No, they agreed not to share expenses. 5. Do you expect to stay long? No, I expect not to stay long. 6.Does he manage to eat much salt? No, he manages not to eat much salt. 7.Have they discussed sending her to camp? No, they've discussed not sending her to camp. 8.Does she enjoy wearing shoes in summer? No, she enjoys not wearing shoes in summer. 9.Did the company consider increasing prices? No, it considered not increasing them. **C:** Suggested answers: 2.She's hoping not to miss the train. 3.They agreed not to smoke. 4.He enjoys not getting up early.

UNIT 39 A: 2.having seen 3.having lost 4.having broken 5.having worked 6.having fooled 7.having told 8.having taken 9.having won 10.having invited **B:** 1.Does he want to have done something famous before his death? No, he just wants to have raised his children. 2.Did Frank promise to have put in a new transmission before 5? No, he just promised to have changed the filter. 3.Does the author expect to have finished his book by January 1? No, he just expects to have written part of it. 4.Did Mr. McNamara pretend to have written the book? No, he just pretended to have read it. 5.Did the student admit having copied his neighbor's test? No, he just admitted not having studied for the test. 6.Does the player remember having left the game? No, he just remembers having scored the winning goal. 7.Did she mention having grown up in Wisconsin? No, she just mentioned having gone to college there. 8.Does your daughter hope to have earned her medical degree by next year? No, she just hopes to have completed most of her course work. 9.Did they resent having been treated like third graders? No, they just resented having been left out of the games. **C:** 2.to have lost weight for the summer 3.to have raised $150,000 4.having picked tomatoes

UNIT 40 A: 1.Are they considering moving to the suburbs? No, they're considering buying a house in town. 2.Are you admitting taking the money? No, I'm admitting seeing it on the table. 3.Is she hoping to get a raise in pay? No, she's hoping to keep her job. 4.Are you preparing to work in business? No, we're preparing to become teachers. 5.Is he risking losing

his life? No, he's risking losing his reputation. 6.Were you agreeing to supply the cement? No, I was agreeing to supply the sand. **B:** 2f.Who is discussing raising the taxes? The city government is discussing raising them. 3e.When was he hoping to graduate? He was hoping to graduate next year. 4b.Where are you planning to go to dinner? We're planning to go to an Italian restaurant. 5a.How many kids are trying to get in the car? About 15 are trying to get in (it). 6d.Whose car is beginning to get old? Mine is beginning to get old. **C:** 1.The medicine has helped to clear my nose, but it hasn't helped to settle my stomach. 2.They've finished building the office, but they haven't finished building the parking garage. 3.She's planned to go to Canada, but she hasn't planned to drive there. 4.I've agreed to help with the park project, but I haven't agreed to do the whole job. 5.She's learned to play tennis, but she hasn't learned to play very well. 6.The city has delayed fixing the streets, but it hasn't delayed raising the property taxes. **D:** Suggested answers: 1.They should start looking/to look for one. 2.She might forget to lock it. 3.The doctor will suggest giving up smoking. 4.She can't stand hearing him practice the violin. 5.They might decide to go to Florida for a while.

UNIT 41 A: 1.We weren't going to skip class. We were going to come in late. 2.I wasn't going to paint the furnace. I was going to clean it. 3.They weren't going to burn the files. They were going to keep them in a safe. 4.Some of the players weren't going to strike. They were going to play ball as usual. 5.They weren't going to block off 18th Street. They were going to block off Lennox Avenue. 6.The company wasn't going to build a plant in Detroit. They were going to buy out a competitor there. 7.The store wasn't going to refund any money. They were going to give people replacements. **B:** 1.No, it was going to be there, but it isn't now. 2.No, I was going to get her a watch/one, but I'm not now. 3.No, she was going to translate all the letters/of them, but she isn't now. 4.No, they were going to go on strike, but they aren't now. 5.No, they were going to reduce it, but they aren't now. 6.No, they were going to use candles/ them, but they aren't now. 7.No, it was going to have an appendix/one, but it isn't now. 8.No, I was going to keep paper/some there, but I'm not now. 9.No, he was going to hunt deer this weekend, but he isn't now. 10.No,

they were going to buy wooden skis, but they aren't now. [Note: In speech the auxiliary *was* or *were* receives loud stress.] **C:** 2.Where was the family going to go? They were going to go to the beach. 3.How many people were going to be at the wedding? One hundred and fifty people were going to be at the wedding. 4.When was Andrew Scott going to speak? He was going to speak at 3 p.m.

UNIT 42 A: 2.is to wear ... is not to put 3.is to appear ... is not to miss 4.is to give ... are not to be 5.was to be ... was not to leave 6.were to collect ... weren't to turn 7.aren't supposed to turn 8.is supposed to be ... isn't supposed to rain 9.are supposed to walk ... aren't supposed to stay 10.is supposed to be ... isn't supposed to have 11.were supposed to win. ... weren't supposed to beat 12.was supposed to type ... wasn't supposed to write **B:** 2.Passengers are supposed to stand behind the white line. 3.Passengers are not supposed to talk to the operator. 4.Passengers are not supposed to smoke on the bus. 5.Passengers are not supposed to spit. 6.Passengers are not supposed to play radios. [Note: This exercise can be extended by using other regulations, e.g., passenger airline regulations, park regulations, highway laws and regulations, etc.] **C:** 2.What's Terry not supposed to drink? She's not supposed to drink coffee. 3.How many pills is Bill supposed to take a day? He's supposed to take two pills daily. 4.Who's supposed to stay out of work for two weeks? Chris Walker is supposed to stay out of work for two weeks.

UNIT 43 A: 1.They didn't use to live there. They used to live in Illinois. 2.There didn't use to be a bakery there. There used to be a bookstore. 3.I didn't use to eat soup for lunch. I used to eat a hamburger. 4.She didn't use to shop there. She used to shop at Murphy's. 5.He didn't use to deliver the *Star*. He used to deliver the *Times*. 6.He didn't use to park there. He used to park on the street. 7.They didn't use to drive on the right side of the road in Sweden. They used to drive on the left. **B:** 1.Did you use to cook your own supper? No, but I used to cook my own breakfast. 2.Did you use to play the trumpet? No, but I used to play the violin. 3.Did you use to walk to work? No, but I used to walk home. 4.Did you use to wear a suit to work? No, but I used to wear a jacket. 5.Did you use to have a pet?

No, but I used to take care of a neighbor's. 6.Did you use to work in a shoe factory? No, but I used to repair shoes. 7.Did you use to camp in the mountains? No, but I used to take hikes. 8.Did you use to go to the horse races? No, but I used to bet on the horses. 9.Did you use to work for a candidate? No, but I used to vote in every election. C: 1.Who did he use to work for? He used to work for Fred. 2.How much did he use to weigh? He used to weigh 170 pounds. 3.How did she use to get to work? She used to take the bus. 4.What did you use to like to watch? I used to like to watch basketball. 5.Where did they use to live? They used to live in Philadelphia. 6.Who did he use to date? He used to date Conchita. 7.Where did they use to swim? They used to swim in the lake. 8.What did they use to make? They used to make machine equipment. 9.How did he use to vote? He used to vote very liberally. 10.Where did you use to get it cut? We used to get it cut at Ernie's Place. [Note: Many native speakers would stress *used to* in this type of response.]

UNIT 44 A: Suggested answers: 1.I wrote it down. 2.They'll have to dream one up. 3.Then she rubbed it in. 4.He didn't fill it up. 5.Then she cut it out. 6.I'll have to think it over. 7.They didn't sort them out. 8.We didn't call it off, though. 9.The wet weather brings them on. **B:** Suggested answers: 1.What can she put it on with? She can put it on with a brush. 2.What can he scare them away with? He can scare them away with a stick. 3.What can they put it out with? They can put it out with water and sand. 4.What can I wash it off with? You can wash it off with some water. 5.What can he dig them up with? He can dig them up with a hoe. 6.What can she pull it out with? She can pull it out with tweezers. 7.What can they close it off with? They can close it off with a rope. 8.What can they tear it down with? They can tear it down with a wrecking ball. **C:** 1.Have they left the posters up? No, they've taken them down. 2.Did you pull out the roots? No, I left them in. 3.Are you going to check out the new restaurant? No, I'm going to check out the new play. 4.Will the children eat up the doughnuts? No, they'll eat up all the candy. 5.Will they fix up that old house? No, they'll tear it down. 6.Is he putting away some money in the safe? No, he's taking some out. 7.Did he bring back your lawn mower? No, he brought my rake back.

UNIT 45 A: 1.Can I count on your attendance? No, you can't count on my attendance/it. 2.Has she fallen for your sweet words? No, she hasn't fallen for my sweet words/them. 3.Did anyone laugh at your old jokes? No, no one laughed at my old jokes/them. 4.Do children take to math easily? No, they don't take to math/it easily. 5.Will you settle for a smaller apartment? No, I won't settle for a smaller apartment/one. 6.Does that company deal in antique furniture? No, they don't deal in antique furniture/it. 7.Are you going to look into the cause of the accident? No, we aren't going to look into the cause of the accident/into it. 8.Have the police come across any interesting clues yet? No, they haven't come across any interesting clues/across any yet. 9.Does his little sister always tell on him? No, she doesn't always tell on him. [Note: When we use the full noun variant, we are disagreeing or insisting. The negative word will be stressed. The pronoun variant is ordinarily used.] **B:** 2.come down with 3.catch up to 4.look out for 5.get away with 6.go back on 7.catch up with 8.look out for **C:** Suggested answers: 1.They're looking into it. 2.He's calmed them down. 3.She told on them. 4.No, she's going to sleep on it first. 5.No, he'll stick to it. 6.Maybe he's come down with something. 7.Yes, he's really fallen for her.

UNIT 46 A: Suggested answers: 2a.Do you know where the post office is? It's on Main Street. 3f.Do you know how a camera works? Light enters the camera and activates the sensitive film inside. 4e.Do you know who discovered the South Pole? The Norwegian Roald Amundsen discovered it. 5j.Do you know when Halley's comet will return? It'll return in about 2056. 6g.Do you know why vaccines work? They build up the body's resistance to disease. 7d.Do you know how much a color TV costs? It costs from $400 up. 8b.Do you know how many passengers a 747 airplane holds? It holds two or three hundred. 9i.Do you know how long the Nile River is? It's over 4,000 miles long. 10h.Do you know how big the Moon is? It's about a quarter the size of the Earth. **B:** Suggested answers: 2.She's thinking about what she wants to do first. 3.She saw how candy bars are made. 4.He's showing her what he baked. **C:** Suggested answers: 2.who he was 3.how a hotel operates 4.what they were saying 5.where she hid it 6.when he was playing baseball

7.where it is 8.when it'll get here 9.how it works 10.which one he should get

UNIT 47 A: Suggested answers: 2.whether I'll buy one 3.whether he paid it or not 4.whether they offer them or not 5.whether she got one 6.whether he went there 7.whether he's going to give one or not 8.whether I turned it off or not **B:** Suggested answers: 2.What's he wondering? He's wondering if he could get a puppy. 3.What are they wondering? They're wondering if a storm is coming. 4.What are they wondering? They're wondering if they passed the exam. **C:** Suggested answers: 2.whether or not he had a beard 3.whether or not we want to buy it 4.whether or not he'll have the operation 5.whether or not she's paid enough income tax 6.whether or not she'll stay 7.whether or not he has enough money for them 8.whether or not he'll run for re-election 9.whether or not it's Portuguese 10.whether or not she is here

UNIT 48 A: Many correct answers **B:** Suggested answers: 2.how to get it 3.what to do now 4.how to do this 5.which one to attend 6.when to invite them 7.what to give him 8.how to get there 9.how to deal cards 10.when to expect it **C:** Suggested answers: 1.I'm not sure whether or not to turn it off. 2.They don't know whether or not to trade in their old car. 3.I don't know whether or not to keep it from her. 4.He's in doubt whether or not to go to the conference. 5.She's doubtful whether or not to get a new one. 6.They're not sure whether or not to eat there. 7.I don't know whether or not to put a new ribbon in it.

UNIT 49 A: 1.I'm going to the doctor because I don't feel well. I'm going to the doctor because of my upset stomach. 2.Food prices are high now because of the dry weather. Food prices are high now because the weather's been very dry. 3.The kids are playing indoors because it's raining outside. The kids are playing indoors because of the rain. 4.Betty left the theater because she didn't like the film. Betty left the theater because of the bad acting in the film. 5.The company moved to Plainfield because taxes are lower there. The company moved to Plainfield because of the lower taxes there. 6.The bus is stuck because of a flat tire. The bus is stuck because one of its tires is flat. 7.He couldn't eat the beans because of all the salt. He couldn't eat the beans because they were too salty. 8.I can't study because it's too noisy. I can't study because of the noise. 9.Mamoru was late because of the heavy traffic. Mamoru was late because the traffic was heavy. **B:** 1.I'm hungry because I didn't have lunch. 2.The weather changed because a cold front moved in. 3.She's smiling because he remembered their wedding anniversary. 4.I eat there because they serve good seafood. 5.She can't paint because the sunlight isn't good today. 6.We're raising our prices because our costs went up. 7.He took his car to the garage because it wasn't running well. 8.They're working on the road because there are holes in it. 9.We need a new scale because this one isn't accurate. 10.She asked him out because he seemed very friendly. **C: Suggested answers:** 1.I couldn't take one because I didn't have any change. 2.She didn't eat it because of her diet. 3.He cried because of his sister's death. 4.It's off because Mother wants to sleep. 5.He can't give us a ride because his car is at the garage today. 6.They don't play outdoors then because of the snow and cold weather. 7.He lost it because he didn't campaign hard enough. 8.It's broken because a branch hit it during the storm.

UNIT 50 A: 1.Since the history teacher was absent, they showed us a film. 2.The dog wasn't very active since it was old. 3.Since there was no rain, we had to irrigate the fields. 4.I've already read the paper since it comes in the morning. 5.He can leave school any time since he finished all his exams. 6.Since she broke her leg, she had to go to the hospital. 7.Since there's no electricity, we can't stay up very late. **B: Suggested answers:** 1.Now that Mr. Fry has left the room, the students are playing. 2.Now that the car is running well again, I drive to work. 3.Now that the weather's getting hotter, we go to the beach every weekend. 4.Now that Laura and Lars are friends, they come to parties together. 5.Since his phone has been busy for two hours, I'll leave him a note. 6.Now that Ms. McGarvey's working downtown, she takes the subway. 7.Since Watkins has published his first book, he's writing another one. 8.Since we'll be picking her up in the car, she'll have more time to get ready. 9.Since I've spent all my money, I have to stay home tonight. 10.Since the boy is sick, he's staying in bed. 11.Since it's time to go, we'd better get our coats. **C: Suggested answers:** 2.I don't have my credit card

with me 3.the weather's going to be nice Sunday afternoon 4.I'm going to the post office today 5.the Eagles have several injured players 6.Mrs. Yates has always been kind to our children 7.she wants to major in industrial architecture 8.she's on an assignment at City Hall

UNIT 51 A: 1.She's taking a shower to get cleaned up. She's getting cleaned up to go to a dance. 2.I went to the library to borrow a book. I borrowed a book to learn about losing weight. 3.Mr. Blake bought a ticket to fly to Newfield. He flew to Newfield to sign a contract. 4.Paul will go to the department store to buy a suit. He'll buy a suit to wear to the wedding. 5.He went to the bank to take out some money. He took out some money to buy a new motorcycle. 6.She got out a shovel to dig a hole. She dug a hole to plant the rosebush. 7.He's working overtime to make some extra money. He's making some extra money to buy a new car. 8.She's selling her car to get $2,000. She's getting $2,000 to pay her bills. 9.I want to borrow the car to go to the swimming pool. I'm going to the swimming pool to cool off. 10.You can go to an ear doctor to get a hearing aid. You can get a hearing aid to improve your hearing. 11.She went to the kitchen to make some coffee. She made some coffee to warm herself up. **B: Suggested answers:** 2.Why was that woman studying? To become a lawyer. 3.Why was that man taking aspirin? To cure his headache. 4.Why was that man in the jewelry store? To buy an engagement ring. **C:** 2d.We made a trap for Harry to catch mice. 3e.Mrs. Hall left a message for the secretary to give to Marisa. 4a.That company publishes books for foreign students to use to learn English. 5b.I have a question for Ms. Fuller to ask the computer. 6f.I'll peel an orange for you to eat.

UNIT 52 A: 1.They bought a second car so (that) they each could use one. 2.They're advertising on the radio so (that) a lot of people will hear about it. 3.Shirley used a lot of fertilizer so (that) she could grow big tomatoes. 4.Miss Lane put on a shower cap so (that) she could keep her hair dry. 5.I took a bus so (that) I could save some money. 6.There's an answer key in the book so (that) students can check their answers. 7.He's hurrying home so (that) he can tell his wife the good news himself. **B:** 2g. 3h. 4f. 5a. 6e. 7d. 8b. **C: Suggested answers:** Why is

Sandy going to buy a soup bone? I don't know. Maybe so she can make some beef soup. Why is Sandy going to buy some blue paint? I don't know. Maybe so she can paint the dining room. Why is Sandy going to buy a bicycle? I don't know. Maybe so she can ride along the bike trail on the weekends.

UNIT 53 A: 2f. 3g. 4b. 5h. 6e. 7c. 8d. **B: Suggested answers:** 1.What will you do if they don't have lasagna? If they don't have that, I'll order spaghetti. 2.What will you do if it's raining hard? If it's raining hard, I'll stay at Steve's. 3.What will you do if the sweater is the wrong size? If it's the wrong size, I'll go back and exchange it. 4.What will you do if they raise your rent? If they raise my rent, I'll look for another apartment. 5.What will you do if the lights go out? If the lights go out, we'll light some candles. **C:** 1.If you turn this handle, an alarm will sound. 2.The police will give you a reward if you give them information. 3.José can run in the race if he brings a letter from his doctor. 4.You can make $100 extra if you work overtime this weekend. 5.I could translate this letter for you if I had my dictionary here. 6.If we can save enough money, we may go to Japan this summer. 7.Take lessons from Mr. Bell if you want to play the trumpet. 8.If you feel dizzy, take this medicine. 9.Eat good food and exercise every day if you want to be healthy. 10.If you need an application form, write to our home office.

UNIT 54 A: 2b. 3e. 4h. 5d. 6a. 7g. 8c. **B:** 1.I'll be in the office tomorrow if I don't have to be in St. Louis. 2.She can't go to the dance unless she promises to be home by midnight. 3.Unless they lower the price, I won't buy the car. 4.If I go to the dentist I don't have toothaches. 5.He can borrow her car if she doesn't have to use it. 6.You can guess at the answers on the test if you aren't sure of them. 7.She's not going out today unless there isn't any food for supper. 8.I'll help you look for your wallet if you can't find it. **C:** 2a.No, I can't open this unless I have a can opener. 3d.No, you won't pass if you don't get better grades. 4e.No, they won't admit her unless her visa is valid. 5c.No, you can't get in if you're not a senator.

UNIT 55 A: 1.No, she won't. But she'd deduct them if she could. 2.No, they won't. But they'd promote him if they could. 3.No, they won't. But they'd borrow it if they could. 4.No, she won't. But she'd bring him if she could. 5.No, we won't. But we'd take a long one if we could. **B:** 1.Would he play if Art and Luis were playing? Yes, he would. 2.Would they refund the money if he had the sales slip? Yes, they would. 3.Would you drink it if it had sugar in it? Yes, I would. 4.Would she go swimming if she had one? Yes, she would. 5.Would you go to Dr. Warner if you liked her? Yes, I would. 6.Would Erik get that job if he finished college? Yes, he would. 7.Would they deliver it today if the drivers weren't on strike? Yes, they would. 8.Would she have time to meet them at the airport if she didn't have so much work to do at the office? Yes, she would. 9.Would you have dessert if you weren't watching your weight? Yes, I would. 10.Would they stay home if the baby weren't sick? No, they wouldn't. 11.Would you have extra money to spend if you didn't need it for a doctor's bill? Yes, I would. 12.Would you park here if you didn't have a special sticker on your car? No, I wouldn't. 13.Would we use your office if they weren't painting the conference room? No, we wouldn't. **C:** Suggested answers: 1.What would you do if you had too much to carry? I'd take a taxi. 2.What would you do if you saw a snake? I'd kill it. 3.What would you do if you found a lot of money? I'd give it all away to my friends. 4.What would you do if you saw an accident? I'd try to help. 5.Where would you go if you needed shoes? I'd go to the shoe store and get a pair. 6.Who would you call if you did not feel well? I'd call the doctor. 7.What would you do if you were late for work? I'd make up the time in the afternoon. 8.Where would you go if you had some free time? I'd go to Bermuda.

UNIT 56 A: 1.Did he get the sunglasses? No, he didn't. But he would have gotten them if he hadn't found his other pair. 2.Could they drive up the mountain? No, they couldn't. But they could have driven up if their car had been running well. 3.Could Carmen write the report? No, she couldn't. But she could have written it if her assistant had tallied the figures. 4.Did they answer the ad? No, they didn't. But they would have answered it if they had had enough money. 5.Did Mr. Burton answer you? No, he didn't. But he would have answered me if he had heard me. 6.Was Ms. Elkins at the meeting? No, she wasn't. But she would have been

there if she'd been feeling well. 7.Did you mail the letter? No, I didn't. But I would have mailed it if I'd had stamps. 8.Were you worried? No, we weren't. But we would have been worried if we had known his background. 9.Could he open the lock? No, he couldn't. But he could have opened it if he had remembered the combination.
B: Suggested answers: 1.If I had run out of gas, I would have called my neighbor. 2.If I had been late for work, I still would have driven carefully. 3.If I had been angry at him, I would have left the room. 4.If I had torn my shirt, I would have mended it. 5.If I had seen it, I would have tried to help. 6.If I had gone to Japan, I would have traveled all around the country. 7.If I had gotten some extra money, I would have put it in the bank. **C:** 2.Because his car had a flat tire. Would he have gone to the party if his car didn't have a flat tire? Yes, he would have. 3.Because her phone was off the hook. Would anyone have called her if her phone wasn't off the hook? Yes, they would have. 4.Because they received small portions. Would the guests have been satisfied if they hadn't received small portions? Yes, they would have.

UNIT 57 A: 2e.I read a lot in spite of my poor eyesight. 3f.The water's cold although the air's quite hot. 4c.Carolyn used that towel although it was already wet. 5h.The Polar Bear Club goes swimming in the winter in spite of the cold. 6b.We bought the $400 encyclopedia although it seemed expensive. 7d.He wore the suit although it was out of style. 8g.The car's engine froze in spite of the antifreeze. **B:** 2.although the traffic was heavy 3.although he was wearing a helmet 4.although the ice was thin **C:** 1.Does your friend look nice? Yes, she does—even though she's wearing old clothes. 2.Did the horses go near the hay? No, they didn't—even though they were hungry. 3.Could you find the planet Saturn? No, I couldn't —even though I had my telescope. 4.Did you recognize Mr. Stone? Yes, I did—even though he tried to hide behind a curtain. 5.Did the kite fly? Yes, it did—even though it didn't have a tail. 6.Does your sister eat peanut butter? Yes, she does—even though she doesn't like peanuts. 7.Did he get another haircut? Yes, he did—even though his hair wasn't very long. 8.Is this milk all right? Yes, it is—even though someone left it out of the refrigerator. 9.Did she drive her car to

work this morning? Yes, she did—even though she couldn't find her glasses.

UNIT 58 A: 1.Yes, it may take him all day, but he's going to find it. 2.Yes, it may take me all day, but I'm going to read it. 3.Yes, it may take her all day, but she'll finish it. 4.Yes, it may take her all day, but she's going to write all of them. 5.Yes, it may take them all day, but they will rebuild it. 6.Yes, it may take her/him all day, but she/he will teach it to them. 7.Yes, it may take him/her all day, but he/she's going to see all of them. 8.Yes, it may take her all day, but she will iron them all. 9.Yes, it may take me all day, but I'll type them all. **B:** Suggested answers: 1.You may have a sore finger, but you have to type these pages anyway. 2.Ms. Sickenberger might have an odd name, but she's very popular anyway. 3.The house might be old, but it's in excellent condition. 4.The play may not have been particularly well written, but it was very effective. 5.They may say they saw a UFO, but I don't believe it. 6.You might have left home on time this morning, but you were late to work anyway. 7.The movie may not have been very good, but she watched the whole movie/the whole thing anyway. 8.The music may not have been played well, but we enjoyed the child's performance anyway. 9.The house might look empty, but there's someone inside. **C:** Suggested answers: 2.but it has modern buildings 3.but she's buying fruit 4.but Contestant 5 won first prize

UNIT 59 A: 2b. such … (that) I couldn't eat it all. 3a.so … (that) he always tried to learn new tricks. 4d.such … (that) it hurt her back. 5f.so … (that) she could hardly walk. 6j.so … (that) few customers could refuse him. 7g.so … (that) she's wearing it out. 8h.such … (that) they're going to move to a larger location. 9e.such … (that) it took me half an hour to get some stamps. 10i.Such … (that) we were afraid to knock on the door. **B:** Suggested answers: 1.No, so few members attended that we couldn't vote on any business. 2.Yes, so much sugar spilled that we needed a broom to sweep it up. 3.No, so little of the fish was unsafe that we were able to make a big profit. 4.Yes, such a lot of people answered the ad that we had to install an answering machine. 5.No, the report took so little time that we were able to work on something else. 6.No, so few plants survived the winter that we had to replant the whole garden. 7.Yes, such a lot of dirt got in the bathtub that it clogged the drain. 8.No, he plays video games so little that his friends think he's strange. **C:** 2.How strong is the wind? It's so strong that it blew the man's hat off. 3.How hard is that man's handshake? It's such a hard handshake that it's hurting the other man. 4.How perfect is that dive? It's so perfect that there is little splash.

UNIT 60 A: 1.No, they're too heavy to lift. 2.No, it's too far away to see. 3.Yes, it's easy enough to do. 4.Yes, they're simple enough to understand. 5.No, I'm too sick to pick them up. 6.No, there was too much to finish. 7.Yes, it was easy enough to fix. **B:** Suggested answers: 1.Is Bobby old enough to get a job? No, he's not old enough for that. (or) No, he's too young for that. 2.Is Mrs. Brown old enough to be retired? Yes, she's old enough for that. 3.Is Ruth Brown too old to drive a car? No, she's not too old for that. (or) Is Bobby too young to drive a car? Yes, he's too young for that. 4.Is Bobby old enough to ride a bicycle? Yes, he's old enough for that. 5.Is Bobby old enough to get married? No, he's too young for that. 6.Is Mrs. Brown too young to ride the bus for free? No, she's old enough for that. 7.Is Ruth Brown too old to take out a life insurance policy? No, she's not too old for that. **C:** 2.The watch is too expensive for her to buy. 3.The bag is not big enough for the letters to fit. 4.She is too young to ride a bike.

UNIT 61 A: 1.Do you insist that he eat everything on his plate? No, I insist that he eat some of each food. 2.Do the Torreses prefer that we visit them next week? No, they prefer that we visit them now. 3.Is the president asking that Congress revise the election law? No, he's asking that Congress change the tax law. 4.Did the police officer order that the man put his hands up? No, he ordered that he put them behind his back. 5.Did they advise that Michaela go into accounting? No, they advised that she take up a musical instrument. 6.Is the school urging that parents stay at home? No, it's urging they visit their child's school. 7.Has the union demanded that the company not hire new workers? No, they've demanded the company not fire any present workers. 8.Has his father insisted that he paint the house? No, he's insisted that he paint the steps. 9.Does the waiter suggest that they order steak? No, he suggests they

order the fish. **B:** 1.Is it advisable that we do that? Yes, it certainly is. 2.Is it suggested that she do that? Yes, it certainly is. 3.Is it better that they do that? Yes, it certainly is. 4.Was it required that he do that? Yes, it certainly was. 5.Was it advisable that you do that? Yes, it certainly was. 6.Was it urgent that he do that? Yes, it certainly was. 7.Was it important that they do that? Yes, it certainly was. [Note: Other questions can be formed that do not use pronouns such as *that*— Is it necessary that he fill out another form? Is it advisable that we install a fire alarm? etc.] **C:** Suggested answers: What's he telling him to cut down on? He's telling him (that) he should cut down on sugar and alcohol. What's he saying not to drink? He's saying (that) he can't drink coffee or tea. What's he suggesting to begin? He's suggesting (that) he begin exercising. What's he advising him to get? He's advising (that) he gets eight hours of sleep a night. What's he telling him to lose? He's telling him (that) he must lose 25 pounds.

UNIT 62 A: 2.had 3.handled 4.were 5.didn't charge 6.had told 7.would be 8.had begun 9.would give/had given 10.would find/had found **B:** 1.I wish she had a compact disc player. I hope she'll get one for her birthday. 2.I wish she played the guitar. I hope she plays the piano. 3.I wish the roads were plowed. I hope the snow isn't too deep 4.I wish there was a mail delivery today. I hope my letter will come tomorrow. 5.I wish the baby weren't crying. I hope he'll stop soon. 6.I wish the files weren't wet. I hope they're still readable. 7.I wish Tom Shipley weren't on vacation this week. I hope he'll return early. 8.I wish the clerk didn't have a cold. I hope it isn't serious. 9.I wish this job didn't take an hour. I hope I can leave by noon.
C: Suggested answers: 2.I wish this dog wasn't here. I hope it doesn't bite me. 3.I wish he wouldn't climb so high. I hope he doesn't fall. 4.I wish I wasn't stuck in this traffic jam. I hope it clears up soon.

UNIT 63 A: 1.I said Bill and Terry were out of town. 2.I said they were taking a computer course. 3.I said he wasn't learning much about life. 4.I said I always took the Fifth Avenue bus. 5.I said it rained almost every afternoon. 6.I said Mercedes blew up 17 balloons. 7.I said they'd turned their TV set off. 8.I said it was going to be cold tomorrow. 9.I said doctors really were busy people. 10.I said there were just a

few wild animals around here. 11.I said we didn't sell typing paper here. 12.I said the experts were not always right. 13.I said she didn't pay her electric bill until the last minute. 14.I said there'd never been an invention like sliced bread. [Note: It is also correct to leave the present tense and not change to past tense after *I said*—I said I'm upset about that news.] **B:** 1. Janet told David she had fixed his lunch. 2.David told Janet he didn't need his lunch. Janet told David he should always eat his lunch. 3.David told Janet that she was having lunch with him downtown today. Janet told David she had forgotten about it. 4.David told Janet that he was glad he didn't forget. Janet said that everyone forgets sometimes. 5.David told Janet that he'd never forget a lunch date with his wife. Janet told David she'd planned a lunch date with a friend, and she wanted a lunch date with him next week.

UNIT 64 A: 1.Did you say you'd be ready at five? 2.Did you say other people wouldn't mind? 3.Did you say I couldn't change my mind now? 4.Did you say she must be quite successful? 5.Did you say we had to order more paper towels? 6.Did you say I could hang my coat here? 7.Did you say he must not spend all his time with Tina? 8.Did you say we couldn't use Summit Avenue? 9.Did you say no one should go outside in this weather without a hat? 10.Did you say it might take more than two hours? 11.Did you say Harold should remember his appointments? 12.Did you say I might not get another chance? 13.Did you say the store would be decorating for Mother's Day next week? 14.Did you say we should be getting an answer from the foundation soon? 15.Did you say they must be spending a fortune on doctor bills? 16.Did you say I should be warming up in the other room? 17.Did you say some of the players might not be returning next year? 18.Did you say he shouldn't have paid the plumber yet? 19.Did you say you must have missed something? 20.Did you say Ms. Tendall wouldn't have done a thing like that? 21.Did you say the schedule wouldn't have changed? 22.Did you say my quarter may/might have fallen into a hole? 23.Did you say the lock could be changed for me? 24.Did you say no one would be left out? **B:** 2.When did Elaine say she could meet Mark? She said she could meet him at 7:15. 3.Which chair did she say might be the best choice for the living room? She said the rocker might be the best choice. 4.What did she say must be notified? She said the insurance company must be notified.

UNIT 65 A: 1.I asked if there were any radios cheaper than this. 2.I asked if you had any cheaper radios. 3.I asked if you wanted to know her address. 4.I asked if you were looking for her address. 5.I asked if the business outlook looked better. 6.I asked if business was going to improve. 7.I asked if that tomato looked ripe to you. 8.I asked if it was time for bed already. 9.I asked if we'd have to go to bed so soon. 10.I asked if you were satisfied with the color of the curtains. 11.I asked if the color of the rug satisfied you. 12.I asked if the dog had been fed. 13.I asked if the dog was eating its food. 14.I asked if John and Akiko could see the pictures. 15.I asked if Mr. and Mrs. Rodríguez were looking at them. 16.I asked if there was a pencil in that drawer. 17.I asked if you saw my red pencil over there. 18.I asked if there were two b's in the name Webber. 19.I asked if the name Webber was spelled with two b's. 20.I asked if there had been any rain this week.
B: 1.She asked how much the color TV with remote control was. 2.He wasn't sure when the book reports were due. 3.He asked what time it was. 4.She was wondering what kind of work Walter did. 5.He asked Jean how she liked the movie. 6.He wanted to know what "frenetic" meant. **C:** Suggested answers: What lap is Pete Hernandez on? I'm sorry, I didn't hear you. I asked what lap Pete Hernandez was on. He's on lap 220. What happened to José Marton's car? I'm sorry, I didn't hear you. I asked what happened to José Marton's car. It had an overheated engine.

UNIT 66 A: 1.I said to come by a little early. 2.I said not to send any flowers to the hospital. 3.I said to finish the homework before class. 4.I said to put sugar in my tea for me. 5.I said not to drive so fast around this curve. 6.I said to write an essay about an interesting experience of yours. 7.I said not to forget your doctor's appointment.
B: 1.Mrs. Ching told/warned the kids to be back before midnight. 2.Mr. Sandquist told Sally to clean the bird cage today. 3.She told Don not to get cigarette ashes on the furniture. 4.He told/begged his mother not to smoke any more cigarettes. 5.Doreen asked the nurse to give her a 2:30 appointment. 6.Mr Walker's doctor told/advised him not to get too much

sun. 7.Peggy told/warned Ali to duck his head. 8.Barbara told Jackie not to say another word on the subject. 9.The sergeant told/ordered the soldier to move a little faster. **C:** Suggested answers: 2.The sign says no left turns between 7 and 9 a.m. on weekdays. 3.The instructions say to lift the receiver, deposit 25 cents, listen for the dial tone, and dial your number. 4.The label says to keep out of the reach of children.

UNIT 67 A: Suggested answers: 2.In other words 3.First/For example 4.For example 5.By the way 6.Therefore 7.However 8.Likewise **B:** Suggested answers: 1.Miss Wan tried to get on the bus. However, the bus was full. 2.It was pouring rain. Therefore, Mr. Ridgeway took his car. 3.I'm not going to leave any. In other words, I'm going to drink all the juice. 4.You don't have suntan lotion on. Therefore, you can't stay in the sun very long. 5.Look at the difference between these bushes. For example, this one has bigger leaves. 6.Ted's putting the model together. However, he's doing it the wrong way. 7.Lightning causes a lot of fires. Likewise, careless campers cause a lot of fires. 8.Neither team scored a goal for 55 minutes. Finally, the Eagles got a point. **C:** Suggested answers: 2.Two plus two equals four, and three plus one equals four. Likewise, one plus three equals four. 3.The sales for November were up. However, the sales for December were down. 4.Howard Jones has experience teaching high school students. For example, he taught at Morton High last year.

UNIT 68 A: 2c. 3h. 4b. 5f. 6e. 7a. 8d.
B: 2.I've brought … that are bothering you 3.that sat next to me … that won a prize in a horse show 4.you're talking about … that has had many disappointments 5.I'm recommending … that have heart trouble 6.we need … that just left 7.I'm giving you … we keep our supplies in 8.that can't run fast … that will protect it **C:** 1.Yes, he opened one that pays interest and one that he can write checks on. 2.Yes, they're sending one that can fix typewriters and one that can fix computers. 3.Yes, she has one that fought for the North in the Civil War and one that fought for the South. 4.Yes, we'll stay at one that has a swimming pool and one that has free movies. 5.Yes, she listens to ones that play country music and ones that play classical music. 6.Yes, he collected ones

that honor famous generals and ones that show famous paintings. 7.Yes, I buy ones that are advertised on TV and ones that my friends tell me about.

UNIT 69 A: 2g. 3c. 4e. 5a. 6d. 7f. 8b.
B: 2a.Yes, we can sit where we sat last time, if you reserve our seats early. 3g.Yes, she can sleep when the shades are up, if it's a dark day. 4b.Yes, he'll move his car so Abdul can get by, if she asks him politely. 5d.Yes, they charge extra when you dial a number, if you talk to an operator. 6c.Yes, we should hurry home so the ice cream won't melt, if it's hot outside. 7h.Yes, they'll clean the air filter when it needs it, if you pay extra. 8f.Yes, they play cards even though they always lose, if they're having fun.
C: 1.No, but I would have looked for them where he/she was playing, if he/she had been playing with them. 2.No, but she would sing so everyone could hear her, if she had a good voice. 3.No, but he would cry before the nurse gave him a shot, if he saw the needle. 4.No, but you could eat while you were watching TV, if you weren't eating watermelon. 5.No, but she could swim if she didn't have one, if she had short hair. 6.No, but they would meet even though he isn't speaking, if it were a regular monthly meeting. 7.No, but I would stay in the club if they raised the dues, if they had more activities.

UNIT 70 A: 1.Although he had promised lower taxes, he had to raise them when he got in office. 2.Although it's hot here, you'll need a sweater when you get to the ocean. 3.Although the bridge was weak, it didn't break when the truck drove over. 4.Although the house isn't painted, I'll take a picture of it when I get a roll of film. 5.Although she's never played an instrument, she'll take clarinet lessons when she gets to high school. 6.Although they usually give refunds, they don't give them when they're having a sale. **B:** 1.Yes, but even though she was happy she cried because it was such a surprise. 2.Yes, but even though he had an accident he wasn't hurt because he had his seat belt on. 3.Yes, but even though she made a mistake in the figures her client didn't get upset because the mistake didn't affect the main points. 4.Yes, but even though they drank some water they got thirsty again because they were working so hard. 5.Yes, but even though I mailed the letters yesterday they'll go out this morning because I missed the last pickup. 6.Yes, but even though the company president likes their soap they'll discontinue making it because it's not selling well. 7.Yes, but even though I need to go to the dentist I won't go this week because I'm very busy. **C:** 2.so … even though 3.Even though … when 4.Even though … as soon as 5.If … even though 6.Even though … before 7.until … even though 8.Although … even though

UNIT 71 A: 1.I'll need a bag lunch when I go to work so I don't have to eat out. 2.I'll need my library card when I go to the library so I can borrow some books. 3.I'll need some stamps when I go on vacation so I can send my friends postcards. 4.I'll need some suntan lotion when I go to the beach so I don't get burned. 5.I'll need a grocery list when I go to the supermarket so I won't forget anything. 6.I'll need warm clothes when I go to Quebec so I'll be comfortable. 7.I'll need some change when I go downtown so I can put it in the parking meter. **B:** 1.Yes, even though it's raining I'll practice so I'll be ready for tomorrow's game. 2.Yes, even though he doesn't like it he'll eat it so he won't displease his host. 3.Yes, even though she doesn't have much time she'll pick us up so we don't have to walk. 4.Yes, even though it was still good I've thrown it away so it wouldn't sit overnight. 5.Yes, even though there was some time left on it he put more money in the parking meter so he could go to the movie. 6.Yes, even though they're not ripe we picked the tomatoes so the birds won't get them. 7.Yes, even though she wasn't interested in it she went to the marketing workshop so she could increase her chances for a pay raise. **C:** 2.If they ask for a donation … so (that) they won't bother us anymore 3.If the storm holds off a while longer … so (that) the grass doesn't get too high 4.If we lose sales to them … so (that) they'll have to change theirs 5.If some books don't sell well … so (that) we can get them off the shelves 6.If you work there for 20 years … so (that) you'll want to work 20 more years 7.If Mr. Hazlett gets a cold … so (that) he won't develop pneumonia 8.If you go out … so (that) I don't have to leave the office

UNIT 72 A: 2.I made … we're giving 3.I can use … I'm writing 4.we planted … they cut down 5.they're giving … they just developed 6.the dog made …

I typed 7.I need … I'm applying for 8.you played … you gave last summer **B:** 2.the pie (that) I made with the apples (that) you brought 3.the page (that) you tore out of the book (that) I lent you 4.the important letters (that) we found in the files (that) we cleaned out 5.the poster (that) Eric designed for the music festival (that) we had last summer 6.the lamp (that) I made out of the large bottle (that) you gave me 7.those things (that) you put in the package (that) we sent 8.the dirt that has gotten on this wall (that) I just painted 9.the tea (that) you made with the tea bag (that) I found 10.the unusual child (that) we saw with the man (that) we met on the subway **C:** 1.Is this the ring that she found in the ground that she dug up? No, it's the one she found in the box of things you sent over. 2.Is this the painting that you did during the week that you were home? No, it's the one I did on the weekend I went to the country. 3.Is this the reward that comes to people that work hard all their lives? No, it's the one that comes to people that are lucky. 4.Is this the reason that's given to customers that ask for a refund? No, it's the one that's given to people that ask silly questions. 5.Is this the name that he gave to the horse that he bought last year? No, it's the one he gave to a ship he designed.

UNIT 73 A: 1.What Mrs. Duncan said to the woman who was sitting next to her made her giggle. 2.What the bus driver said to the man who was sitting in the back seat made him smile. 3.What Marjorie said to the man who was fixing her TV made him angry. 4.What Mr. Hutchins said to the man who was watching him made him frown. 5.What the teacher said to the student who was chewing gum made him/her embarrassed. 6.What Miguel said to the people who were teasing him made them furious. 7.What Lynn said to the man who was mowing the park lawn made him happy. 8.What Miss Whitney said to the salesman who was calling on the phone made him angry. 9.What the nurse said to the child who was crying made him/her laugh. 10.What I said to the neighbors who were having a noisy party made them annoyed. **B:** 2a.I haven't heard how they made the kite that they won the contest with. 3b. 4d. 5f. 6e. 7c. 8h. **C:** 1.Wasn't it unusual how Betty solved the problem that was worth ten extra points? 2.Wasn't it unusual how

quickly we got the package that they sent on Monday? 3.Wasn't it unusual how much money he paid for the shirt that he wore to the party? 4.Wasn't it unusual where I found those footprints that lead to the cabin? 5.Wasn't it unusual what they feed these monkeys that perform tricks? 6.Wasn't it unusual what he asked that woman who sat next to him? 7.Wasn't it unusual where she dried out her shoes that she had gotten wet? 8.Wasn't it unusual how she loosened the window that was stuck? 9.Wasn't it unusual why she helped the man who was traveling with five children?

UNIT 74 A: 2.because she admires a candidate that has a lot of experience in politics 3.whenever there was a speech that was long and dull 4.when I drive on streets that have few stop signs 5.if they have a salesman that speaks Spanish 6.because she took a course that trained her in physical therapy 7.because eating them helps to keep you healthy 8.where you see a building that's being built **B:** 2gy. 3dt. 4cx. 5hz. 6bw. 7fs. 8ev. **C:** 2.handles that can break easily 3.a bouquet that has a few red and yellow roses 4.food that has hot spices in it 5.a place that's wet and muddy 6.work that's important 7.the day that he plays golf 8.a job that lasts until 7 p.m. 9.a teacher that had five years' experience

UNIT 75 A: 1.I'm reading about Susan B. Anthony, the woman who led the suffragette movement. 2.I'm reading about Leonardo da Vinci, the man who painted "Mona Lisa." 3.I'm reading about Marie Curie, the woman who discovered radium and won the Nobel Prize. 4.I'm reading about Rudolf Diesel, the man who invented the Diesel engine. 5.I'm reading about Gertrude Ederle, the woman who swam the English Channel. 6.I'm reading about Catherine the Great, the woman who ruled Russia from 1762 to 1796. 7.I'm reading about Herman Melville, the man who wrote *Moby Dick*. 8.I'm reading about William Addis, the man who invented the toothbrush. 9.I'm reading about Harriet Tubman, the woman who organized the "Underground Railroad" to help slaves escape. 10.I'm reading about Roald Amundsen, the man who discovered the South Pole in 1911. **B:** 2it. 3by. 4cq. 5jz. 6gv. 7hu. 8es. 9dx. 10aw.